*Traveler's Guide to H*

*Retreats in Nort*

# Traveler's Guide to Healing Centers and Retreats in North America

Martine Rudee and Jonathan Blease

**John Muir Publications**
Santa Fe, New Mexico

John Muir Publications, P.O. Box 613, Santa Fe, NM 87504

First edition. First printing

**Library of Congress Cataloging-in-Publication Data**

Rudee, Martine, 1958-
  Traveler's guide to healing centers and retreats in North America/Martine
and Jonathan Blease. — 1st ed.
      p.   cm.
    ISBN 0-945465-15-7
    1. Alternative medicine—North America—Directories. 2. Retreats—North
America—Directories.    I. Blease, Jonathan, 1958-
II. Title.   III. Title: Guide to healing centers and retreats in North America.
R733.R83   1989                                                         88-43532
362.1'78 02473—dc19                                                        CIP

Typeface: Trump Medieval
Typesetter: Copygraphics, Santa Fe
Designer: Joanna V. Hill
Printer: McNaughton-Gunn
Maps and cover illustration: Holly Wood

Cover illustration from a painting by David Milby.

Distributed to the book trade by:
W.W. Norton & Company, Inc.
New York, New York

"The natural healing force in each one of us
is the greatest force in getting well"

—Hippocrates

This book is dedicated to
the spirit/healing force within all of us

# Contents

# Acknowledgments

Thanks to Bill Stott for his friendship, Cordon Bleu cooking, and unconditional hospitality; Black Cat; Rick and Lorin; Steve, Jean, and Breeze; Jim Emmott, for being Jim; Shanti for a very special friendship; Darrell for his love and magical way with animals and nature; Marcia, Jessie, Colin, and Alyssa Phipps for their caring and support; Lynn and Florence Rudee; Cyndi, Tracy, Terri, and their families (especially Kristopher, Kelly, and Jacob); Bill and Jay's magical Zen garage; Phil Sotter for his generosity and support; Charley and Tracy; Toby and Virginia for providing us with such a wonderful "taste" of New Mexico and for their love and incredible support; Myra for her "specialness"; RAM Corporation, especially Emily and Anita; Michael Bertrand, Jennifer King, Jeffrey Joseph, Ron Benenati, Megan Hill, Nancy Gott, Marjorie Miller, Shelbee Matis, and Betsy Dodge for their support and assistance during the first stages of the book; Maggie for her encouragement and caring; Tony and Jennifer Blease; Sally, Mandy and Nicki; Bobby, Stewart, Laibrook, Kai, and Mikkel Bernstein; Lannis and Joseph for their inspiring letters; Jan, Rita, Tinne, Robbe, and Lise for being in Africa; and, finally, a huge thank you to all the centers and retreats in the United States and Canada that responded to our questionnaire, especially to those that sent words of encouragement and praise.

# Introduction

**Travel**—to go from one place to another; journey (through)

**Heal**—to restore or return to health; cure

**Center**—a place of concentrated activity or influence

**Retreat**—a quiet, private, or secure place; refuge

It is our belief that the world has become a place where the healing of the individual and the planet is of utmost importance. By "healing," we mean the attainment and maintenance of peace on all levels (e.g., physical, mental, emotional, and spiritual)—inner peace and outer peace both with ourselves and with everything around us.

Life in Western society has become for many of us the exact opposite. It has become full of stress, and its highly technological nature makes it tend toward the impersonal and uncaring. Fortunately, there are many people who feel this concern, and are doing something about it. Healing centers and retreats are but one example of a growing network of those who believe in peace and in providing a facility where people can get away from the stress of their lives, find healing, and bring it back with them on their return.

Our aim in producing this book is to make these healing centers and retreats more available to all people, for to our knowledge there is no other work like this in print. The centers and retreats we have been able to list in detail all responded to a questionnaire in which we had listed the criteria used in compiling this book. The criteria are as follows:

1. Centers must actively encourage and/or assist participants to discover and strengthen their own healing powers (e.g., through workshops, classes, seminars, and/or support groups).
2. Retreats must provide an environment to allow participants to reestablish an inner balance (e.g., through reconnecting with themselves and their own healing powers and the healing powers of Nature).
3. The principles of both centers and retreats should be of a (w)holistic, nondenominational nature, ultimately leading the person to health on all levels (physical, mental, emotional, and spiritual).

We are aware that this is not yet a complete list of healing centers and retreats in the United States and Canada, though we would like it to be in the future. We are also aware that the centers and retreats are growing and changing constantly. It is our hope to compile an updated edition in spring 1990. To do so, we must rely on the cooperation and support of the centers and retreats to let us know they exist and wish to be included in this book. We must also rely on you, the reader and visitor, to let us know of any center or retreat you feel should be included. For this purpose, a questionnaire is provided at the back of the book. You may tear it out and send it back to us with a brochure of your center and/or retreat.

In compiling this first edition, we sent out two or three mailings to 750 centers and retreats. We received information from only 250. Three hundred fifty are listed by name and address only, and 150 had either gone out of business or had left no forwarding address. Needless to say, this has been a difficult project.

Our wish for this guide is that it becomes a valuable tool for finding peace, health, and healing on all levels. Good health—being at peace with ourselves and everything around us—is our natural state. If our book can assist people to again find good health and peace, then it will be successful and we will be fulfilled.

Please send any comments, criticisms or information regarding this book and/or other centers and retreats to New Light Productions, c/o John Muir Publications, P.O. Box 613, Santa Fe, NM 87504.

# *How to Use this Book*

This book has been designed to be an easy-to-use, quick-reference guide to healing centers and retreats in the United States and Canada. The centers and retreats are grouped by region. Within each region, they are listed in alphabetical order, first by state and, second, by town, city or village within each state. (We have taken some liberty in our division of the United States into regions. They are not split exactly on conventional or traditional lines.)

Each region is introduced with a map showing the locations of all the centers and retreats listed in detail in the following pages.

At the end of each regional section, there is a list, "More Centers and Retreats," which is again listed alphabetically by state and then by town within each state. (We were unable to treat these centers and retreats in more detail because they did not respond to our inquiries.)

Following is the main directory, a list of publications, and an extensive glossary. The publications are listed in the same way as the main directory, by region and then alphabetically by state, town, city, or village within each state. We have tried to make the glossary as complete as possible, covering all the different methods and techniques used by the centers and retreats.

# Part I: The Northwest

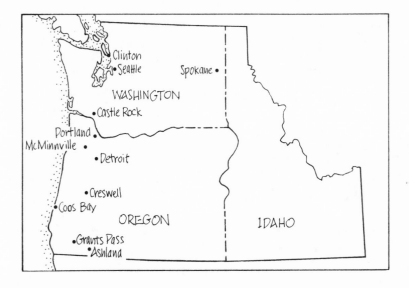

# Aletheia Psycho-Physical Center

1809 N. Highway 99, Ashland, OR 97520
(503) 488-0709

*Hours:* 9:00 a.m.–5:30 p.m., Monday–Friday
*Person to Contact:* Jack Schwarz, President
*Founder/Owner:* Jack Schwarz (1958)
*Purpose:* Health education and research dedicated to increasing harmony, health, and happiness in the world by bringing forth integrative changes in individuals. Our programs, supported through research, educate people in practical and effective methods for achieving optimal health through self-regulation and self-management.
*Facilities:* Eleven thousand square feet of classroom and office space.
*Services:* Seminars, workshops, lectures, personal health training, individual health assessments, and massage institute.
*Visions and Goals:* To develop an integrated health center.
*Materials Available:* Books, tapes, and videos.


# Ken Keyes College

790 Commercial Avenue, Coos Bay, OR 97420
(503) 267-6412

*Hours:* 8:30 a.m.–5:00 p.m., Monday–Friday
*Founder/Owner:* Ken Keyes, Jr. (1982)
*Purpose:* The teaching and practice of unconditional love through the Living Love system and the Science of Happiness.
*Facilities:* Located in Coos Bay on the Oregon coast, the college is self-contained with student, staff and guest housing, food service and dining, and complete teaching and training facilities.
*Services:* A variety of personal growth workshops with emphasis on teaching specific methods that can be used in everyday life to promote cooperation, happiness, and heart-to-heart loving feelings.
*Materials Available:* Books and cassette tapes by Ken Keyes, Jr. Music cassettes and posters.

# Breitenbush Hot Springs Retreat and Conference Center

P.O. Box 578, Detroit, OR 97342
(503) 854-3314 or 371-3754

*Hours:* 9:00 a.m.–7:30 p.m., Monday–Friday
*Person to Contact:* Peter Moore or Alex Beamer, Co-directors
*Founder:* Alex Beamer (April 1977)
*Owner:* Breitenbush Hot Springs Co-op
*Purpose:* To offer retreats, workshops, and conferences on all aspects of human potential and actualization. We are working for positive evolution, both personal and social-cultural, and to create a model of a self-reliant community of people. We are a very eclectic group who live and work at the Springs. The essential qualities of spirit— honesty and respecting the dignity of oneself and others—are our common ground. We are open year-round and invite individuals, couples, and families as well as groups and events.
*Facilities:* Eighty-five acres of forestland, with the Breitenbush River running through the middle of it, containing some 40 hot mineral springs. (We generate our own electricity from the river, space heating from geothermal heat exchange, etc.) Large and elegant old mountain hotel-lodge and 60 cozy cabins with double and triple occupancy surrounded by old firs and cedars on a bluff above the Breitenbush River. Some cabins can accommodate up to six people. Meeting facilities, Medicine Wheel hot tubs, steam sauna, and the sanctuary, which is used for prayer, meditation, yoga, and music. Hiking trails, cross-country skiing, old growth wilderness, and swimming hole on river.
*Services:* Some examples of retreats offered at Breitenbush are Massage Retreat with workshops on Intention, Focus, and Direction in massage work with Susan Kerr Shawn and Yoga as a Tool For Centering with Julie Godmestad, RPT; Yoga and Self-Healing Retreat with Shoshanah Thielle; Training of the Heart with Barry and Joyce Vissell; Women's Retreat with Melanie Crocker and Tamara Oglesby; Men's Retreat with Thomas Fisher, M.S., Jack Crocker, L.M.T., and Conrad Zevely; and Tai Chi Retreat with Chris Luth. Some examples of workshops are Making Your Own Music with Jim Scott; Imagery in Healing with Peg Mayo, R.C.S.W.; Creating Successful Relationships with Donna Miller; and Hakomi Therapy Workshop with Jon Eisman.

Also offered are daily yoga and meditation, therapeutic massage, three delicious, wholesome, vegetarian meals each day, 24-hour use of hot springs baths (outdoors) and steam sauna, and child-care. Volunteer Work Program, 40-hour workweek in exchange for room, board, and an experience of community life. Easter at Breitenbush, put on by the Breitenbush staff. Memorial Day weekend, a chance to welcome summer. Annual Healing Retreat, limited to 300 adults.

*Visions and Goals:* To continue with the original vision of creating and offering to this society a place of both exquisite beauty and healing in all forms—a place transformative both for those who live there and those who come to visit.

*Materials Available:* Audiovisual equipment, maps of surrounding wilderness, hiking, and skiing areas, and educational materials of all kinds.

*Miscellaneous:* Breitenbush is not just "another roadside attraction." Consistently, the people who come to Breitenbush experience a spiritual energy that illuminates life, strengthening and restoring them for "the city," which is where most of us must live.

# Center for Well-Being

82644 Howe Lane, Creswell, OR 97426
(503) 895-2953

*Hours:* Mornings and evenings, Monday–Friday
*Person to Contact:* Gary Reiss or Barbara Hurwich, Co-directors
*Founder/Owner:* Barbara Hurwich and Gary Reiss (1983)
*Purpose:* To create an opportunity for people to live together who share an interest and background in organic gardening and the healing arts.
*Facilities:* Eleven acres in a beautiful country setting 20 minutes from Eugene, Oregon. Greenhouse, organic gardens and orchard, animals and old growth trees, two seminar rooms, two treatment rooms, several houses, cabins, and yurts.
*Services:* We specialize in process-oriented psychology, a unique approach to mind-body healing that integrates dream, body, and relationship work, meditation, and working with world issues into a single theoretical framework. We teach this work ourselves and bring other people to teach it in seminar format. We also offer seminars in organic gardening and in working with group process in intentional communities. Individual consultations and specialized workshops offered.

# Aesculapia

1480 Dutcher Creek Road, Grants Pass, OR 97527
(503) 476-0492

*Hours:* 7 days a week
*Founder/Owner:* Jeanie Eagle and Graywolf Swinney (December 1983)
*Purpose:* A contemporary Aesculapian Dream Healing Temple providing personal and group retreats for healing, spiritual evolution, and transformation as well as a research and training center for exploring nonordinary states of consciousness and their relationship to healing and living.
*Facilities:* Guest lodge, seasonal camping, wood-heated sauna, meditation decahedron, library, hiking trails and old growth stands, and power spots.
*Services:* Dream healing rituals, weekends, and weeklong workshops. Solstice, Equinox, Thanksgiving, and other gatherings; spiritual healing; and training for ordination in the healing ministry. "Gathering of Healers" yearly conference. "Gatherings" newsletter. Vegetarian meals.

## Planetary Smile

511 E. 3rd Street, McMinnville, OR 97128
(503) 472-8815

*Hours:* 10:00 a.m.–5:30 p.m., Tuesday–Saturday; 10:00 a.m.–7:00 p.m., Friday
*Person to contact:* Joyce Marvel
*Founder/Owner:* Joyce Marvel (August 20, 1986)
*Purpose:* To support and encourage introspection and expression of personal truth and power.
*Facilities:* Store with meeting and relaxation room and therapy room.
*Services:* Classes, workshops, and retreats on all types of personal growth; community networking.
*Visions and Goals:* To continue to love people.
*Materials Available:* Books, tapes (500 sampler tapes), crystals, ritual tools, incense, video and audio rentals.

## Center for Holistic Medicine

2104 N.E. 45th Avenue, Portland, OR 97213
(503) 287-7727

*Hours:* 8:00 a.m.–5:00 p.m., Monday–Friday
*Person to contact:* Dr. Martin Milner, Director
*Founder/Owner:* Dr. Milner (September 1983)
*Purpose:* To optimize health and prevent disease with natural therapeutics and preventive and holistic medicine.
*Facilities:* 1,200-square-foot building, full laboratory, pharmacy, physical therapy equipment.
*Services:* Heart physicals, monitor massage, orthopedics, manipulation nutrition, women's health, allergies.
*Visions and Goals:* To spread holistic and naturopathic medicine to as many people as possible.

# Common Ground, Inc., and Inner City Hot Springs

2927 N.E. Everett Street, Portland, OR 97232
(503) 238-4010

*Hours:* 9:00 a.m.–10:00 p.m., 7 days a week.
*Person to Contact:* Lary Graves, Manager, Inner City Hot Springs, or Audy Davison, Receptionist for Common Ground
*Founder:* David Slawson (1976)
*Owner:* Collective
*Purpose:* To provide an in-city, accessible center for relaxation, healing, reconnecting and finding nurturing and quiet.
*Facilities:* Hot tubs and sauna (Inner City Hot Springs), flotation tanks, garden, workshop and class space.
*Services:* Ten licensed massage technicians offering massage and body work, 1 Aston patterner offering structural rebalancing, 2 chiropractic physicians, 4 counselors offering gestalt, Hakomi, NLP, and inner child work, 1 psychic counselor, and 1 rebirther. Ongoing yoga and movement classes, support group, plus various workshops and classes.
*Visions and Goals:* To continue to expand.

# Cloud Mountain

373 Agren Road, Castle Rock, WA 98611
(206) 274-4859

*Hours:* 8:00 a.m.–6:00 p.m., 7 days a week
*Person to Contact:* Anna or David Branscomb, Managers
*Founder/Owner:* Anna and David Branscomb (February 1984)
*Purpose:* To provide facilities and a serene and conducive environment for groups and individuals wishing to engage in longer-term, intensive meditation practice.
*Facilities:* Both single and dormitory-style rooms accommodating up to 35 people including teachers and staff; two meditation/meeting halls; fully equipped kitchen and dining hall; communal shower house and sauna. A rural, semirustic, and comfortable environment with ponds, walking paths, garden and farm animals.
*Services:* Meditation retreats led by teachers from many contemplative traditions, including Zen, Vipassana, Tibetan Buddhist, and Taoist.
*Visions and Goals:* To offer instruction and ongoing guidance in meditation and provide opportunities for deeper and more extended practice.
*Materials Available:* Book and tape library available for guest use.

# Chinook Learning Center

Box 57, Clinton, WA 98236
(206) 321-1884 or 467-0384 from Seattle

*Founded:* 1972
*Owner:* Nonprofit organization
*Purpose:* The central dynamic of Chinook ("warm wind blowing") is education—the training and empowerment of people who are endeavoring to bring positive change to the world.
*Facilities:* Located on 64 acres of evergreen forest and meadowland, the facilities include a restored farmhouse and cedar-log sauna, three small cabins, a newer retreat house, camping area and bathhouse, an orchard and two gardens. Offices, resource center, Warm Wind Bookstore and Madrona Restaurant located in nearby Clinton. Chinook Waldorf School.
*Services:* Programs led by Chinook staff, guest facilitators from across the continent, and members of our associate faculty, internationally known educators, theologians, artists, ecologists, and social innovators with whom we have a collegial relationship.
*Materials Available:* A wide selection of books and music, cards, jewelry, crystals, children's books, and tapes of Chinook educational programs.

# The Albintra Wellness Center/Natural Medicine Works

438 N.E. 72nd, Seattle, WA 98115
(206) 522-9384

*Hours:* 9:00 a.m.–6:00 p.m. (or 7:00 p.m.), Monday–Saturday
*Person to Contact:* Corinne Dee Kelly or Jerry Chroman, Practitioners
*Founder/Owner:* Jerry Chroman, Ken Powell, Corinne Dee Kelly, Gwen Crowell, Francine Loeb (October 1982)
*Purpose:* The Center's purpose is summed up in the meaning of Albintra, "emanating from within." Natural Medicine Works is a caring family health service offered by naturopathic physicians.
*Facilities:* Naturopathic clinic, massage therapy rooms, sauna, classroom space.
*Services:* Preventative medicine, nutritional assessment, diagnostic services, homeopathy, counseling, botanical medicine, traditional Chinese medicine, Swedish massage, deep tissue, trigger point shiatsu, reflexology, touch for health, rebirthing, Trager, and edukinesthetics. Classes on a variety of health-related topics.
*Visions and Goals:* The underlying theme of our services is to help you let go of mental, emotional, and physical pain and tension.

## Astrology Et Al
4728 University Way N.E., Seattle, WA 98105
(206) 524-6365

*Hours:* 10:00 a.m.–6:00 p.m., Monday–Friday; 10:00 a.m.–5:30 p.m.,
  Saturday
*Person to Contact:* Laura N. Gerking, Manager
*Founder/Owner:* Maggie Nalbandian (April 1975)
*Purpose:* Service to the metaphysical community.
*Facilities:* Classrooms for a variety of subjects, bookstore and gift
  store.
*Services:* Classes and workshops; counseling in astrology, tarot, psy-
  chic, runes, numerology, and palmistry. Sponsor of the Northwest
  Astrological Conference (yearly).
*Visions and Goals:* Service to the ever-growing metaphysical commu-
  nity in the state of Washington. To present a wide variety of
  metaphysical ("New Age") ideas and concepts to the general public.
  Goal: to eventually have a complete University of Metaphysical
  Thought.
*Materials Available:* Books and gifts.

---

## Light Works
7011 California Avenue S.W., Seattle, WA 98136
(206) 932-1408

*Hours:* 11:00 a.m.–6:00 p.m., Monday–Saturday
*Person to Contact:* Kenneth Davis
*Founder/Owner:* Kenneth Davis (November 1987)
*Purpose:* To act as a gathering place and information center on alterna-
  tive spirituality.
*Facilities:* Bookstore, classroom, and healing/meditation room.
*Services:* Rebirthing, Reiki, astrology, tarot, classes, lectures, and
  counseling.
*Visions and Goals:* To create a point of light in the spiritualization of
  mankind and to provide information on all spiritual paths.
*Materials Available:* Books, tapes, supplies, and art. Network with sev-
  eral of the other Seattle centers.

# The Northwest Center for Holistic Medicine

4072 9th Avenue N.E., Seattle, WA 98105

(206) 547-9665

*Hours:* 9:00 a.m.–5:30 p.m., Monday–Friday (for physicians, counseling, and massage). Also evenings and weekends and separate schedules for sauna and hot tub use.

*Person to Contact:* Dr. Judyth Reichenberg-Ullman or Dr. Robert Ullman

*Founder/Owner:* Dr. Robert Ullman and Dr. Judyth Reichenberg-Ullman (August 1985)

*Purpose:* To offer comprehensive, individualized holistic health services that support and heal body, mind, emotions, and spirit in an atmosphere of love and acceptance.

*Facilities:* A beautiful, older home in Seattle's University District including hot tub, sauna, and colon therapy facilities. Classroom and hot tub/sauna spaces are also available for private rental.

*Services:* Naturopathic, homeopathic, Ayurvedic and family medicine, chiropractic, acupuncture, psychotherapy, hypnosis, massage, polarity therapy, midwifery, past life therapy, astrological and spiritual counseling, stop smoking/weight loss programs, hot tub, sauna, colon therapy, fasting, and cleansing programs.

*Visions and Goals:* Our vision is to bring together a harmonious group of spiritually and service-oriented holistic health professionals to help people reach their highest potential of health and healing on all levels. We provide education on many aspects of natural living and spiritual transformation. We also wish to provide the public with a beautiful and healing hot tub/sauna facility in which they can escape from the stresses of life in the world.

*Miscellaneous:* Our comprehensive cleansing and fasting programs are unique in that they combine detoxification methods of Western naturopathic medicine with Ayurvedic Pancha Karma. Programs last from 3 to 15 days, and overnight lodging can be arranged. We are often looking for additional staff members and have a space that accommodates up to 30 for seminars.

## Bear Tribe Medicine Society

P.O. Box 9167, Spokane, WA 99209
(509) 326-6561

*Hours:* 9:00 a.m.–5:00 p.m., Monday–Friday
*Person to Contact:* Beth Davis, Director
*Founder:* Sun Bear (1970)
*Owner:* Nonprofit corporation
*Purpose:* To teach respectful caretaking of the earth and healthier and more self-reliant ways of living through tapping ancient wisdom of native peoples of this continent and elsewhere in the world.
*Facilities:* Rustic mountain center; tent, tipi camping, solar showers, and outhouses. Mail order bookstore.
*Services:* Personal growth intensives; classes on ceremony for healing self and earth; vision quest for adults and teens; gardening, perma-culture, and self-reliance courses. Healthful meals. Speakers' bureau.
*Visions and Goals:* To help bring balance to people's lives and to life on the planet so that we can change course from life-destructive to life-affirmative.
*Materials Available:* Networking magazine, *Wildfire*, books by Sun Bear and other Bear Tribe members.

# More Centers/Retreats

## Idaho

*Heart Center* 1306 Eastman, Boise, ID 83702 (208-342-9963)
*The Open Path* 703 North 18th Street, Boise, ID 83702
(208-342-0208)
*Red River Hot Springs* Elk City, ID 83525
*Bald Mountain Hot Springs* Box 426, Ketchum, ID 83340
(208-726-9963)
*Lava Hot Springs Foundation* Lava Hot Springs, ID 83246
(208-776-5221)

## Oregon

*Awehai Center* 230 S.W. 3rd Street, Corvallis, OR 97333
(503-758-0330)
*The Center for Well Being* 82644 Howe Lane, Creswell, OR 97426
(503-895-2953)
*Woman's Healing Ground* 37010 S.E. Snuffin Road, Estacada, OR
97023 (503-630-7848)
*Lifelong Learning Excellence* Box 380, Eugene, OR 97440
(503-343-1202)
*Mountain Grove Center* Box 105, Glendale, OR 97442
(503-832-2871)
*Hunter's Lodge* Box 950, Lakeview, OR 97630 (503-947-2127)
*Open Door New Age Center* 1644 N.E. Highway 101, Lincoln City,
OR 97367 (503-994-2488)
*Belknap Hot Springs* Box 1, McKenzie Bridge, OR 97401
(503-822-3535)
*Atlantis Rising Health Education* 7915 S.E. Stark Street, Portland,
OR 97215 (503-253-4031)
*Healthworks* 2917 N.E. Everett Street, Portland, OR 97232
(503-231-0090)
*Phoenix Rising* 333 S.W. 5th Avenue, #404, Portland, OR 97204
(503-223-8299)
*Ritter Hot Springs* Box 16, Ritter, OR 97872 (503-421-3846)
*Kathapos-Center for Wellness* 1665 Liberty Street S.E., Salem, OR
97302 (503-873-5771)
*Wy'East Healing Center* P.O. Box 1031, Sandy, OR 97005
(503-668-7698)
*World Peace University* Box 188, Sweet Home, OR 97386
(503-367-2249)

**Washington**

*Lorian Association*   Box 663, Issaquah, WA 98027 (206-641-3846)

*Resort of the Mountains*   1130 Morton Road, Morton, WA 98356 (206-496-5885)

*Biba Hot Springs*   1 Cascade Road, N. Bonneville, WA 98639

*The Olympic Center*   P.O. Box 7534, Olympia, WA 98507 (206-456-3078)

*Sol Duc Resort*   Star Route 1, Box 11, Port Angeles, WA 98362

*Institute for Consciousness & Music*   Box 173, Pt. Townsend, WA 98368 (206-385-6160)

*Daybreak Star Center*   P.O. Box 99100, Seattle, WA 98199 (206-285-4425)

*Friends of EKR*   18210 15th N.E., Seattle, WA 98155 (206-362-6290)

*Lodestar Center*   11049 8th N.E., Seattle, WA 98125 (206-364-3395)

*NW Center for Attitudinal Healing*   11700 1st Avenue N.E., Seattle, WA 98125 (206-362-3897)

*Psychosynthesis Center*   311 W. McGraw, Seattle, WA 98119 (206-282-1171)

*Resource Institute*   2370 Fairview Avenue East, Seattle, WA 98102 (206-325-7300)

# Part II: The Pacific

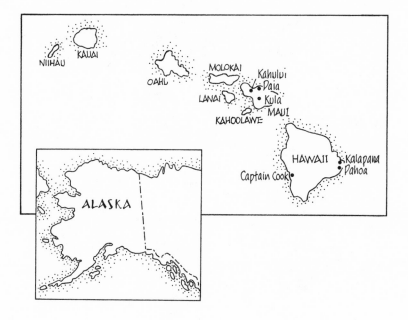

# The Maui Center for Attitudinal Healing

P.O. Box 134, Kahului, HI 96732
(808) 878-2945

*Hours:* 9:00 a.m.–5:00 p.m., Monday–Friday
*Person to Contact:* Ellie Fry, Clinical Director
*Founder/Owner:* Originally founded in Tiburon, California, by Dr. Jerry Jampolsky (1975)
*Purpose:* To supplement traditional health care by providing an environment in which both children and adults faced with life-threatening illness can actively participate in the process of attitudinal healing. The concept of attitudinal healing is based on the belief that it is possible to choose peace rather than conflict and love rather than fear.
*Facilities:* Center, bookstore, and gift store.
*Services:* Children's programs; children's group, siblings group, and sons and daughters group, young adult program, adult programs; adult group, adult support group, bereavement support group, and wellness group; educational programs; volunteer program, Attitudinal Healing Training Conference, presentations/workshops/consultations, and contracted services.
*Materials Available:* Books and tapes by Dr. Jampolsky and others.

# Mele Mauka Center

P.O. Box 946, Captain Cook, HI 96704
(808) 328-2207

*Hours:* 24 hours a day, 7 days a week
*Person to Contact:* Joni Choo, Director
*Founder/Owner:* Solomon Choo (1975)
*Purpose:* Yoga, dance and music center. Oceanfront vacation rental retreat.
*Facilities:* Center is located in Houpaloau, 5 miles from the fishing village of Milolii.
*Services:* Ongoing classes and private lessons including classical yoga, Middle Eastern dance, jazz with vocals.
*Visions and Goals:* To establish an international connection for classical yoga, dance, and music. We have a divine interest in establishing an international yoga connection, to allow free growth in the paths of devotion, service, peace and patience, which above all, allows us to reach and be close to the creator in all of us.

# Kalani Honua International Conference and Retreat Center

R.R. 2, Box 4500, Kalapana, HI 96778
(808) 965-7828

*Hours:* 8:00 a.m.–8:00 p.m., 7 days a week, open all year
*Person to Contact:* Humberto Blanco, National Program Director
*Founder:* Richard Koob (1980)
*Owner:* Nonprofit
*Purpose:* Our purpose is to host and develop programs that affirm the sacredness of life and to provide a beautiful, healthful environment conducive to intensive experimental learning.
*Facilities:* 20 acres bordered by jungle and undeveloped coastline. Four 2-story cedar lodges each with kitchen and meeting facilities. 25 meter pool, jacuzzi, sauna, volleyball, tennis court, cafe and gift shop. Accommodations for groups of up to 80. Dance studio.
*Services:* A venue for workshops, seminars and conferences, festivals and performances, as well as individual vacation/retreats. Tours and excursions to local sacred sites. Food service for groups with specific needs. Massage and body work available. Working guest program.
*Materials Available:* Gift shop sells natural fiber clothing, crafts, books, Hawaiiana, tapes, and pereos.

# Heavensong

P.O. Box 450-T, Kula, HI 96790
(808) 878-6415

*Hours:* 9:00 a.m.–5:00 p.m., Monday–Friday
*Person to Contact:* Michael or Maloah Stillwater
*Founder:* Michael and Maloah Stillwater (1978)
*Owner:* Nonprofit spiritual organization
*Purpose:* To inspire, awaken, and support the awareness of the indwelling Spirit and provide opportunities for healing, transformation, and joy.
*Facilities:* Heavensong Retreats are currently held at Kalani Honua Retreat Center in Kalapana, Hawaii, several times a year and frequently at retreat centers throughout America.
*Services:* Weeklong retreats in Hawaii offering inner renewal, relaxation, and inspiration, with music, song, group sharing, yoga, meditation, and leisure time. Delicious vegetarian meals are included. These retreats are often co-led by popular author and teacher Alan Cohen. Heavensong also offers celebrations and worship services, recordings and publications, counseling, and wedding and blessing ceremonies.

# Re-Creation Center aka Hale Mauli Ola Hou

P.O. Box 1653, Pahoa, HI 96778
(808) 965-9880

*Hours:* 24 hours a day, 7 days a week
*Person to Contact:* Marilyn or Bill Rodgers, Co-Directors
*Founder/Owner:* Marilyn and Bill Rodgers (1981)
*Purpose:* An exclusive spiritual healing center. We are continually in the process of creating and maintaining a safe and supportive environment in which people can transform and let go of fear, stress and negative conditioning to discover how loving and capable they really are.
*Facilities:* Beautiful five-acre location on the ocean, with accommodations for 20-30 people, resource library, pool, hot tub, sauna, fruit, nuts, organic vegetable garden, and beautiful views. Hot ponds for underwater birthing training. The Alright Family Band and Entertainment Network office.
*Services:* Underwater birthing, preparation, rebirthing, and conscious breathing sessions. Yoga-martial arts, nutritional awareness, bed and breakfast, tour to the volcano, massage therapy. Two-week, eight-week, and individual programs. Vegetarian meals served.
*Materials Available:* Videos and cassettes.

# Strong, Stretched and Centered

P.O. Box 758, Paia, HI 96779
(808) 575-2178

*Hours:* 24 hours a day, 7 days a week
*Person to Contact:* Gloria Keeling, Director
*Founder/Owner:* Gloria Keeling (September 1980)
*Purpose:* A holistic body-mind program designed to acquaint people with their physical, mental, emotional, and spiritual beings. Also, to certify people to teach fitness if they so desire.
*Facilities:* We house our students in condominiums on a beautiful beach. Classes are held in a nearby dance studio.
*Services:* Two- and four-week programs, and complete six-week trainings.
*Visions and Goals:* Body/mind training in every major city, first, in North America and then throughout the world. By 1990, we will have schools in Atlanta, Georgia, Littleneck, New York, and Monaco.

# More Centers/Retreats

**Alaska**
*Friends of EKR*   P.O. Box 80, Palmer, AK 99645 (907-745-3751)

**Hawaii**
*Hale Akua*   Star Route 1, Box 161, Haiku, Maui, HI 96708
   (808-572-9300)
*Friends Of EKR*   333 Queen Street, #710, Honolulu, HI 96813
   (808-526-4008)
*Kauai Attitudinal Healing Center*   P.O. Box 1330, Koloa, HI 96756
   (808-245-1996)
*Hawaiian Health Haven*   c/o The Vegetarian Society, P.O. Box 441,
   Yucca Valley, CA 92286 (800-628-2828)

# Part III: California

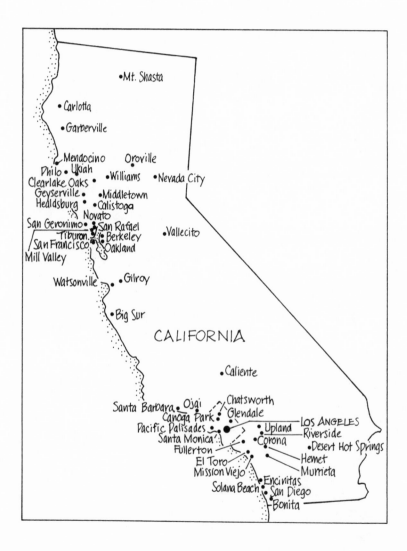

# Berkeley Holistic Health Offices

3099 Telegraph Avenue, Berkeley, CA 94705
(415) 845-4430

*Hours:* 9:00 a.m.–5:00 p.m., Monday–Friday
*Person to Contact:* Mark Abelle
*Founder/Owner:* Dr. Keith Barton (1981)
*Purpose:* To provide holistic health care. Also working with the treatment of AIDS/ARC and immune disorders.
*Facilities:* Medical offices.
*Services:* Internal medicine, chiropractic, acupuncture, Chinese herbology, massage therapy, hypnotherapy, optometry, podiatry.
*Visions and Goals:* To continue to provide quality health care utilizing both traditional and nontraditional methods and protocol provided by individual practitioners: Keith Barton, M.D., CA; Surya Bolom, D.C.; James Lerner, CA; Bobbie Lewis, CA, MT, Dipl. Ac.; Mark Abelle, Dipl. Ac., MT, C.H.; Janie Evans, O.D.; Mardi Merrick, O.D.; Harvey Lampell, D.P.M.; Ken Densmere, CA.

# Biofeedback & Family Therapy Institute

2236 Derby Street, Berkeley, CA 94705
(415) 841-7227

*Hours:* 8:00 a.m.–8:00 p.m., Monday–Friday
*Person to Contact:* Erik Peper and Joan Levy, L.C.S.W.
*Founder/Owner:* Erik Peper, Ph.D.
*Purpose:* Optimal health, mental and physical. Biofeedback and self-regulation for stress management, psychotherapy and family therapy. Holistic in nature, our therapeutic and educational programs enhance awareness and mobilize self-healing.
*Facilities:* Four treatment rooms in self-contained building. House in residential area.
*Services:* Biofeedback, self-regulation and relaxation training, family therapy, pain management, and acute stress relief. Psychotherapy: insight, gestalt, bioenergetic, and Reichian. We specialize in asthma, hypertension, GI problems, hyperventilation, and anxiety.
*Visions and Goals:* To offer a systems perspective to behavioral medicine that treats individuals within the context of their personal, familial, and social situations.
*Materials Available:* Biofeedback instruments, educational material, symptom-related relaxation exercises.

# Berkeley Massage Associates

1962 University Avenue, Berkeley, CA 94704
(415) 845-5998

*Hours:* 10:00 a.m.–10:00 p.m., Monday–Sunday

*Founder:* Anne Parks (1969); Berkeley Massage Studio (1971) was further inspired by Gail Stewart.

*Owners:* Sage Appel, Virginia Withall, Sue Holper, et al. In 1982 became Berkeley Massage Associates.

*Purpose:* To provide the most supportive environment for both giving and receiving massage. To provide brief retreats into oneself so that individual clients may contact their own source of healing with a practitioner's assistance. To provide a support circle for our own healing from which we extend the principle of self-responsibility in making whole the body-mind as well as in healing social and environmental imbalances. To extend into the public awareness the value of touch in keeping ourselves well and healing our dis-ease and injury.

*Facilities:* Three attractive and comfortable massage rooms in a Victorian-style building in downtown Berkeley; two private baths, with old-fashioned tubs; also lounge/office space with bath and kitchen for the associates' use.

*Services:* Individual retreats of 1½ to 2 hours with a complimentary bath in mineral salts, choice of beverage, and massage with a trained practitioner in Swedish/Esalen style massage and one or more of the following body work approaches: acupressure, shiatsu, deep tissue work, foot reflexology, crystals, orthobionomy, polarity, Reiki, Rosen Method, or Trager. We are pleased to discuss your healing and growth process and to refer you to other practitioners.

*Visions and Goals:* To expand our educational function through demonstrations and classes of body work and massage and movement education; talks and experiential gatherings on related approaches; and use of written materials and the media to increase public awareness on the value of touch in human well-being. To create a network of centers for touch, including individual body work sessions, support group for body workers, and educational outreach on the value of touch and other approaches to healing and growth.

*Miscellaneous:* We have a bulletin board where we post announcements and listings of classes, cultural and political events, lectures, body work and meditation schools and groups, and as much networking from our clients as we can include.

One person's experience of the Berkeley Massage Associates: "As I enter into the arched doorway, I am ushered into a space of peace and tranquility. . . finding myself surrounded by soothing pastel colors and a spacious, airy atmosphere. My practitioner is attentive and caring. She offers me herbal tea, plum wine, or spring water while I settle into a hot mineral bath in the old-fashioned clawfoot tub. I am surrounded by plants, and as I soak, I begin to feel at home here. In ten or fifteen minutes, my practitioner leads me into a comfortable Victorian-style massage room. I look around and appreciate the thoughtful touches of fresh flowers, candlelight and the artwork on the walls. As I lie down on the large comfortable massage table, my practitioner asks me to share with her any needs that may come up for me during the session. I feel the total focus of her attention on me, creating a safe and nurturing place for me to let go. My mind is quieted by the soothing music and all the while I am aware that the masseuse is sensing and responding to the changes in my body. Now that my session is finished, my practitioner encourages me to take a few moments for myself before getting up. I sink a little further into the table, closing my eyes again, finding a new sense of self. . .I feel relaxed and whole. . .I am refreshed and revitalized. I realize the value of this session for me is on the inner level, a true gift to myself."

## Nyingma Institute

1815 Highland Place, Berkeley, CA 94709
(415) 843-6812

*Hours:* 8:00 a.m.–6:00 p.m., Monday–Friday
*Person to Contact:* Jack Petranker, Dean
*Founder/Owner:* Tarthang Tulku (1973)
*Purpose:* To provide teaching on human development inspired, in part, by Tibetan Buddhism.
*Facilities:* A large, gracious building high in the Berkeley hills, with a sweeping view of the San Francisco Bay, providing facilities for meditation and instruction, a bookstore, a library, comfortable residential rooms, a meditation garden, all adorned with the healing power of prayer wheels, prayer flags, and Tibetan sacred art.
*Services:* Residential retreats and training programs of one week to ten months duration in Kum Nye relaxing and self-healing, Nyingma meditation, and human development. A full program of day and evening classes, weekend seminars, and other activities, work-study programs, special projects, and instruction by mail. Fine vegetarian meals offered.
*Materials Available:* Audiocassette tapes, books by Dharma Publishing, sacred art reproductions, greeting cards, and gifts.

## Attitudinal Healing Center of San Diego

5736 Good Karma Lane, Bonita, CA 92002
(619) 565-7172

*Hours:* 7 days a week
*Person to Contact:* Mimi Breaux, President
*Founder/Owner:* Mimi Breaux (March 1986)
*Purpose:* The Attitudinal Healing Center of San Diego provides a safe, loving environment to help individuals, families, and friends to experience inner peace in the face of life-threatening or serious chronic illness. The support services supplement traditional health care and professional counseling.
*Facilities:* Currently meeting in private homes of participants or other available space in the San Diego area.
*Services:* Support groups are available on a donation basis. Educational classes and programs are offered on a fee basis. Individual counseling or healing assistance also available.
*Materials Available:* Information about the philosophy, approaches, and services. Resource listing of books, audiotapes and videotapes, and related materials. Some materials for sale or rental.

# Esalen Institute

Big Sur, CA 93920
(408) 667-3000

*Hours:* 10:00 a.m.–3:00 p.m., Monday, Tuesday, Thursday, and Saturday; 10:00 a.m.–12 noon, Wednesday and Friday; 12 noon–8:00 p.m., Sunday

*Founder/Owner:* Michael Murphy and Richard Price (1961)

*Purpose:* To provide a place that supports emotional education, somatic disciplines, and spiritual practices and also assists and encourages the individual in the development of sensory, emotional, interpersonal, kinesthetic, volitional, and spiritual training. Workshops allow participants to explore Esalen's four major areas of concern: the body, the mind, the emotions, and the soul.

*Facilities:* Workshop attendees are accommodated in rooms of two or more persons. Workshop fees include workshop tuition, food, and lodging. Esalen is located in a breathtaking setting at the ocean's edge. The grounds include natural hot baths, a swimming pool, a lodge where meals are served, and a meditation house. Child care is available at the Gazebo School situated on the property, for a fee and with advance reservations.

*Services:* Weekend, five-day, seven-day, two-week, three-week, and month long workshops and intensive training sessions on numerous subjects. (Send for catalog for full details.) For those who wish to live and work at Esalen for a longer period, an extended student residential program is offered. Activities also include consulting and research.

*Visions and Goals:* Esalen Institute is a center to explore those trends in education, religion, philosophy, and the physical and behavioral sciences which emphasize the potentialities and values of human existence. This is done in an atmosphere that remains an open system, encouraging inquiry and exploration rather than adhering to a single point of view.

*Materials Available:* The Esalen Bookstore sells books, tapes, and other items.

# Double D Ranch

Star Route, Box 14, Caliente, CA 93518
(213) 434-3453

*Hours:* 10:00 a.m.–6:00 p.m., Monday–Friday
*Person to Contact:* Caryl Larkins, Office Manager
*Founder/Owner:* Damien Simpson (1980)
*Purpose:* A place of sanctuary and a place for spiritual unfoldment.
*Facilities:* Located on 150 acres of beautiful magical land, accommodations in three spacious dormitory rooms, double occupancy rooms or trailers.
*Services:* Hot tub, massages, and an extensive metaphysical library. All meals are provided. All food is home-cooked with love and pride.
*Visions and Goals:* A metaphysical center to assist anyone in personal growth and development. To many of us this is a place of sanctuary. Man builds cathedrals to get God's attention. God creates nature to get our attention. City life, daily business as usual, and relationship pressures all take their toll on our bodies, minds, and spirits. At the Double D Ranch, one can truly see the stars. Their beauty lifts not only your eyes but also your spirit. The trees and the brooks whisper of life, and at sanctuary, you are invited to sit and play in the grass.

# Dr. Wilkinson's Hot Springs

1507 Lincoln Avenue, Calistoga, CA 94515
(707) 942-4102

*Hours:* 8:00 a.m.–5:00 p.m., 7 days a week
*Person to Contact:* Mark Wilkinson
*Founder/Owner:* Dr. John Wilkinson (1952)
*Purpose:* Stress reduction in a relaxing and comfortable environment.
*Facilities:* Located in charming downtown Calistoga, Dr. Wilkinson's Hot Springs has three beautiful pools: a hot mineral whirlpool located in a glass-walled room filled with tropical plants and ferns, a warm outdoor mineral pool, and a cooler outdoor mineral pool.
*Services:* Mud baths, mineral whirlpool baths, natural mineral steam rooms, blanket wraps, therapeutic massage, skin care, and lodging.
*Miscellaneous:* Mud baths, as done at Dr. Wilkinson's, are one of the most effective ways to transfer heat to the body. The combination of heat and weight transfers heat, thereby allowing for deep muscular relaxation and stress release.

## Amiya Institute
8627 Lubao Avenue, Canoga Park, CA 91306
(818) 998-3702

*Hours:* 9:00 a.m.–5:00 p.m., Monday–Thursday
*Person to Contact:* Raylah Hammond, President
*Founder/Owner:* Raylah Hammond (December 1980)
*Purpose:* Holistic healing center offering alternative healing methods.
*Facilities:* Healing center with classroom facilities.
*Services:* Laying-on-of-hands healing, intuitive channeling, acupuncture and Chinese herbal medicine, past life regressions, reflexology, meditation attunement with masters for world healing.
*Visions and Goals:* Healing on a planetary level.
*Materials Available:* Books, tapes, candles, incense, and posters.

## Center for Feeling People
10170-4 Larwin Avenue, Chatsworth, CA 91311
(818) 882-7404

*Hours:* 10:00 a.m.–10:00 p.m., Monday–Friday
*Person to Contact:* Ivan Arnove or Reisa Winston
*Founder/Owner:* Paul J. Hannig, Ph.D. (1973)
*Purpose:* To facilitate in-depth self-discovery and transformation through experiential methods, cognition, and primal integration.
*Facilities:* Beautiful, fully soundproofed facility.
*Services:* Individual, couples and group sessions; amplified telephone counseling; weight-loss and stop-smoking programs; The Caring Self Program, which consists of ongoing seminars for personal development. The essential areas explored include physicality, intellect, emotions, sensuality, interaction, context, nutrition, and spirituality.
*Materials Available:* Our book *Feeling People*, a large library of discourse and self-help audio-cassettes and catalog and R.E.M. state music tapes.

# Church of Loving Hands, Inc./Metis Medicine Circle

111 Orchard Lane, Carlotta, CA 95528
(707) 768-3226

*Hours:* 10:00 a.m.–4:00 p.m., Monday–Friday
*Person to Contact:* "SKYHAWK" Rev. Rosalind Beal-Ojala, Director
*Founder:* "SKYHAWK" Rev. Rosalind Beal-Ojala, D.D., Metis Pipe Carrier of Blackfoot and Chippewa heritage (April 1982)
*Owner:* Nonprofit, Interdenominational Church of Natural Healing and Medicine Ways
*Purpose:* Loving Hands' primary tenet is to facilitate individual spiritual growth and development by the practices of spiritual expression in all daily activities of life. We are dedicated to the research and ministering of natural earth healing by following the ancient ways of the ancestors of our land and combining them with New Age techniques and teachings. We foster the ancient rituals of bathing and sweating for cleansing and purification. We acknowledge humans as threefold beings: mental, physical, spiritual, with the body as the temple of the soul.
*Facilities:* Four acres on the Van Dusen River in the redwoods of Humbolt County. Tent camping available only; gatherings in the summer months only. Maximum capacity: 20 people. Outdoor kitchen currently with a ½-acre garden.
*Services:* Medicine healing circles, sweat lodge ceremonies on the river, personal shamanic counseling, hands on healing, certification program in massage therapy, classes in psychic development, psychic readings, and counseling. Wilderness gatherings and Vision Quests.
*Visions and Goals:* Future expansion to include outdoor hot tub, sauna, outdoor showers, wooden sleeping platforms, and a large indoor Medicine Lodge for winter gathering with a large community kitchen. Small intimate healing and retreat center where people can come to retreat and get in touch with their hearts and learn to re-own their inner power and purpose for being and reestablish their interrelationship with all our relations, the plant, rock, tree, four-leggeds, winged ones—all our relations according to natural law.
*Materials Available:* Cedar and sage smudge sticks, sweet grass braids, metaphysical library, the sacred teachings of the Medicine Wheel, cassette tapes of songs and chants of the Medicine Circle.

# Revivaria

P.O. Box 862, Clearlake Oaks, CA 95423
(707) 998-1366 or 988-1742

*Hours:* 9:00 a.m.–5:00 p.m., Monday–Friday
*Person to Contact:* Lynda Davis, Facilitator
*Founder/Owner:* Lynda Davis (March 1988)
*Purpose:* To provide support and a space for self-healing through fasting, cleansing, and purification techniques.
*Facilities:* Revivaria is located on beautiful Clearlake. Both indoor and outdoor accommodations as well as use of the hot tub and sweat lodge are available.
*Services:* Fasting retreats that include fresh fruit and vegetable juices and wheatgrass juice. Pranaguma (intentional breathing), deep tissue body work, body alignment, drumming circle, Native American sweat lodge ceremony, hydrotherapy in a garden setting on lake.
*Visions and Goals:* In 1957, Clearlake was aerially sprayed with DDT, becoming one of the first of the major ecological disasters in California. There is an effort toward putting the healing energies generated here at Revivaria back into the lake and the land.

# Emissaries of Divine Light/Glen Ivy Community

25000 Glen Ivy Road, Corona, CA 91719
(714) 735-8701

*Hours:* 8:00 a.m.–5:00 p.m., Monday–Saturday
*Person to Contact:* Achal Bedi, Adminstrator, or Eric Dunn, Educational Director
*Founder/Owner:* Emissaries of Divine Light by Lloyd Arthur Meeker (1932). Glen Ivy Community by John C. Gray (1977).
*Purpose:* The Emissaries of Divine Light provides an educational service through a series of introductory mailings. Glen Ivy Community is the Emissaries regional educational facility. To receive these mailings write: EOS, c/o Sunrise Ranch, 5569 North City Road 29, Loveland, CO 80537.
*Facilities:* Sixty-five acres with a number of California Mission-style buildings, an adjacent hot springs area, and resident staff.
*Services:* A 5-day seminar, The Art of Living, is open to anyone, though enrollment is limited to about 20 people. The seminar is for men and women who are ready to take personal responsibility for their experience in life.

# *We Care Health Center*

18000 Long Canyon Road, Desert Hot Springs, CA 92240
(619) 251-2261

*Hours:* 9:00 a.m.–6:00 p.m., 7 days a week
*Person to Contact:* Susana Lombardi, President
*Founder/Owner:* Susana Lombardi (1985)
*Purpose:* A professional holistic group, devoted to the ultimate in well-
ness, spirituality, and awareness education.
*Facilities:* Five-acre ranch in peaceful, serene, colorful Palm Springs
Desert area. Brand new, spacious facilities.
*Services:* "Body cleansing," a natural way to a healthier you. A 7-day
program to revitalize body, mind, and spirit. Daily yoga, meditation,
nutrition, fasting, massage, reflexology, colon hygiene, beauty treatments, herbs, iridology, and emotional, spiritual, and physical
cleansing.
*Visions and Goals:* We Care is unique in its love, caring and sharing of
only the finest intensive programs to bring you to the experience of
achieving and maintaining zestful health.

## Attitudinal Healing Center of Southern California

24432 Muirlands Boulevard, El Toro, CA 92630
(714) 556-8000

*Hours:* 9:00 a.m.–9:30 p.m., Monday–Friday
*Person to Contact:* Dan Millstein, Co-director
*Founder:* Originally founded by Gerald Jampolsky, in Tiburon, California (1975)
*Purpose:* To provide a safe environment for exploring the possibility that there is another way to perceive the world.
*Facilities:* Meeting rooms for up to 80 people, medical and psychological offices, pharmacy.
*Services:* Group attitudinal healing meetings, individual counseling, seminars, classes on Eastern and Western medicine.
*Visions and Goals:* To create health and inner peace.
*Materials Available:* Books and tapes.
*Miscellaneous:* Attitudinal support groups are at no charge. We are supported by donations and "financial families."

## The Helix Center

22821 Lake Forest Drive, El Toro, CA 92630
(714) 859-7940

*Hours:* 9:00 a.m.–8:00 p.m., Monday–Friday; 11:00 a.m.–6:00 p.m., Saturday–Sunday
*Person to Contact:* Leonard Cohn, Executive Director
*Founder:* Anne Marie Cohn, R.N. (November 1974)
*Owner:* Nonprofit organization
*Purpose:* To provide a safe setting for the creative exploration of body, mind and spirit. The purpose of this exploration is to realize our potential for health, inner peace, compassionate growth, and rewarding personal and global relationships.
*Facilities:* Two fully equipped meeting rooms and a bookstore that offers books in a wide selection of interest related to body, mind, and spirit.
*Services:* (1) seminars that meet from four to eight consecutive weeks; (2) ongoing courses that meet continually throughout the year; (3) part-day, one- or two-day weekend workshops.
*Visions and Goals:* See Purpose, above.
*Materials Available:* Educational materials include books, audiotapes, and videotapes.

# Wellness Now

24432 Muirlands Boulevard, Suite 111, El Toro, CA 92630
(714) 768-3343

*Hours:* 10:00 a.m.–6:00 p.m., Monday–Friday
*Person to Contact:* Dr. Michael Grossman, Director
*Founder/Owner:* Dr. Michael Grossman (June 1988)
*Purpose:* To create health and inner peace. Our main principle of health is that by treating the imbalance in your body/mind, symptoms of ill health can disappear effortlessly and positive changes occur easily. Our center is committed to combining the best of Eastern and Western medicine.
*Facilities:* Office and practitioner rooms located in the Muirlands Medical Center just off the San Diego Freeway.
*Services:* Acupuncture/acupressure, acupressure clinic, Ayurveda, family practice, herbs, hypnosis, massage, meditation, nutrition, right/left brain integration, Trager body work. We offer a 3-level program of personal health care, free and ongoing attitudinal healing support groups, and workshops for mastery of health, by which we mean mental-emotional-spiritual and physical breakthrough.
*Visions and Goals:* "What lies behind us and what lies before us are tiny matters compared to what lies within us." (Emerson)

# Vital-Life Training Institute

954 Capri Road, Encinitas, CA 92024
(619) 436-9642

*Hours:* 9:00 a.m.–5:00 p.m., Monday–Friday
*Person to Contact:* Steve or Annie Schechter
*Founder/Owner:* Steve and Annie Schechter (February 1988)
*Purpose:* To offer training in a wholistic life-style for a nominal charge and to qualify for a State License.
*Facilities:* Center for Total Health.
*Services:* Massage and massage training, yoga, and nutritional counseling.
*Visions and Goals:* To offer a detoxification clinic.
*Materials Available:* Numerous videos on massage, wholistic health, and healing.
*Miscellaneous:* We are a state-approved school of massage located in beautiful southern California. We have operated a school of massage in Arkansas for the past eight years and have graduated over 600 students. Massage is becoming an important tool for personal growth.

## Crystal Light Center
419 W. Commonwealth, Fullerton, CA 92632
(714) 526-3239

*Hours:* 9:00 a.m.–5:00 p.m., Monday–Friday
*Person to Contact:* Elisha Gabriell, Owner
*Founder/Owner:* Antien and Elisha Gabriell (September 1987)
*Purpose:* To serve as an outlet and an education center for crystals.
*Facilities:* Retail store and classroom and healing room.
*Services:* Classes, healing/channeling sessions. The center hosts "12th
Ray Healing," which utilizes crystals and minerals, interdimensional work, sound vibrations, and past life clearing to allow
wholeness.
*Visions and Goals:* To be a center where people can come to find the
goals they need to assist them in their own inner path of self-
realization.
*Materials Available:* We are the largest retailer of crystals and minerals
in Orange County . We also carry wands and other metaphysical
tools, and have an extensive bookstore.

## New Age Reflections
7353 Monterey Street, Gilroy, CA 95020
(408) 848-8210

*Hours:* 10:00 a.m.–6:00 p.m., Monday–Saturday
*Founder/Owner:* Paul Boyd and Anna English (September 1987)
*Purpose:* To be sensitive to the spiritual transformation of the planet
and to help individuals along their path.
*Facilities:* Metaphysical resource center.
*Services:* Classes, workshops, and massage by appointment.
*Visions and Goals:* To assist individuals on their spiritual paths and to
consciously help in the healing of the planet.
*Materials Available:* Metaphysical information, crystals, healing
stones, books, unique gifts, New Age music, and local arts and
crafts.

# Heartwood Institute, Ltd.
220 Harmony Lane, Garberville, CA 95440
(707) 923-3182 or 923-2021

*Hours:* 9:00 a.m.–5:00 p.m., Monday–Friday
*Person to Contact:* Reception, Shivani or Nyra
*Founder:* Bruce Burger (1978)
*Owner:* Robert Fasic and Roy Grieshaber
*Purpose:* Heartwood Institute is a community of individuals who
share a common vision. Our mission is to provide resources for
attaining higher physical, psychological and spiritual well-being.
Our intent is to act as a catalyst for planetary healing through personal transformation. This is accomplished through programs of
study, workshops, and wellness retreats offered to both professionals
and the general public.
*Facilities:* Located on 200 acres of rolling mountains, meadows, and
forests of Douglas fir, live oak, and madrone. The setting may be
described as rustic, rural, and profoundly beautiful. The hot tub,
wood-fired sauna, and large pool are important recreational facilities. The log lodge has a large deck where meals are served in nice
weather. A cozy indoor dining room complete with grand piano
make the lodge a warm place for gatherings. Flower and herb gardens
add a wonderful dimension of color and freshness. Guest rooms are
small and simple. Campsites are available. Meals are pure and
mostly vegetarian, with seafood served twice weekly.
*Services:* Treatment sessions are available in Neo-Reichian massage,
polarity therapy, Swedish massage, deep tissue massage, Tuei-Na
massage therapy, yoga and stretching, educational kinesiology, radi-
ance breathwork, transformational therapy, shiatsu acupressure, Jin
Shin Jyutsu, tarot readings, crystal healing, alchemical hypnosis,
NLP/Ericksonian hypnotherapy, fasting and detoxification programs, and nutritional counseling.
*Miscellaneous:* The unique aspects of Heartwood Institute are that we
are a residential school (those who study here live here for the
length of their study), the staff and faculty are a community living
here with a common purpose, our trainings emphasize personal
transformation, and we are located in a very beautiful California
mountain wilderness area. Heartwood Institute is the center for
professional training in massage therapy, hypnotherapy, transformational therapy, natural health counseling, polarity therapy, Oriental
healing arts and nutrition. The core of our educational training is
our 3-, 6-, and 9-month programs.

# Isis Oasis Lodge and Cultural Center

20889 Geyserville Avenue, Geyserville, CA 95441
(707) 857-3524

*Hours:* 24 hours a day, 7 days a week
*Person to Contact:* Lora Vigné, Owner
*Founder/Owner:* Lora Vigné (1980)
*Purpose:* To connect all those passing through with Mother Nature by means of the environment and animals and birds that they can interact with on the grounds. We also offer a global outlook through our cultural evenings.
*Facilities:* Twelve-room lodge with dormitory and huge carpeted meeting space, retreat house, cottage, tower, barrel house, yurts, tipi, pyramid with accommodations for 80. One hundred seat theater, dining pavilion with commercial kitchen on 10 acres of grounds. Mini-zoo of exotic birds and animals. Pool, sauna, three spas, and a library.
*Services:* We provide space for those who do weekend or residential workshops in healing arts, therapeutic endeavors, theatrical activities, and celebrations marking the passages of life. The Isis Society for Inspirational Studies offers unique theater events with ongoing presentations.
*Visions and Goals:* Isis Oasis would lend itself well to a school where one could study myth and magic of ancient civilizations in conjunction with a focus on health, harmony, and balance in living.
*Materials Available:* Video, hi-fi, easels, blackboards, stage lights, piano, tapes, tables, and chairs.
*Miscellaneous:* Isis Oasis has an ancient Egyptian atmosphere and has recently added an Egyptian Temple that anyone may use for meditation and healing. A 500-year-old fir tree is the centerpiece of the land and creates a magical environment.

# Rainbow Connection for Attitudinal Healing and Learning

444 Piedmont Street, #309, Glendale, CA 91206
(818) 241-0691

*Hours:* 7:30 p.m.–9:30 p.m., 1st and 3rd Thursdays
*Person to Contact:* Renée Riendeau, Director
*Founder/Owner:* Renée Riendeau (February 1986)
*Purpose:* To supplement traditional health care and education by providing an environment of a nonjudgmental, loving attitude toward self and others through 12 principles of attitudinal healing.
*Facilities:* We meet in the director's home at present. We are looking for a different location.
*Services:* Adult support groups, individual children's sessions, volunteer training, and person-to-person support.
*Visions and Goals:* To become nonprofit, to continue to serve the community, and to locate a professional office/building to meet in.
*Materials Available:* Cassette tape of purpose and principles and VHS rental of "Fight for Your Life" by Bernie Siegel, M.D.

# Meadowlark

12626 Fairview Avenue, Hemet, CA 92343
(714) 927-1343

*Hours:* 9:00 a.m.–2:00 p.m., Monday–Friday
*Person to Contact:* Dorothy Soar or Jean Jerome, Co-directors
*Founder:* Evarts G. Loomis, M.D. (February 1958)
*Owner:* Friendly Hills Fellowship, a nonprofit organization
*Purpose:* Spiritual nourishment and physical well-being of the total person: body, mind and spirit.
*Facilities:* Twenty-four guest rooms, dining room, 2 libraries, swimming pool, hot tub, exercise room, lecture hall, chapel, and holistic medical center, with James Kwako, M.D., as director.
*Services:* Psychological counseling, spiritual counseling, polarity therapy (deep massage), yoga instruction, medical assistance, meditation, and wholesome vegetarian-style diet.
*Visions and Goals:* By doing our part to make the world a better place in which to live, our hearts will be more open to the essence of who we are.
*Materials Available:* Books on such subjects as philosophy, religion, psychology, health, nutrition, and spirituality. Audio- and videotapes on the above subjects.

# Life Action Institute
250 Healdsburg Ave., Healdsburg, CA 95448
(707) 433-8365

*Hours:* 11:00 a.m.–6:00 p.m., Monday–Saturday (or by appointment)
*Person to Contact:* Sati-Alwyn, Director.
*Founder/Owner:* Sati-Alwyn, Ph.D. (1988). (Sati-Alwyn is also the
owner of Firewind, Northern California's original Metaphysical
Emporium.)
*Purpose:* The center has been created to meet the needs of people seeking self and of nurturing one's exploration on new paths. Designed
for discovery and reawakening of the past, present, and future paths
one is to follow.
*Facilities:* In its infancy, the center is defined within the walls of Firewind. At present, there is space for reading, a library, a conversation
area, an enclosed tent area for tarot, and so forth, and one room big
enough for small workshops.
*Services:* Sati-Alwyn, Ph.D., works with people subtly, in a departure
from standard techniques. Hers is a shamanic healing of the 4th
Chakra (love of self and others), utilizing a variety of methods, from
tarot to healing circles. Many people associated with Firewind and
the institute are available for consultation.
*Visions and Goals:* The awakening of self is the goal. As the institute
is able to expand (space-wise), a variety of workshops, classes, consultants, and teachers will become available on a more regular basis.
*Materials Available:* Firewind and the Life Action Institute make
available myriad healing, growing, visionary and celebratory tools:
crystals, tarot cards, runes, books, tapes, games, drums, medicine
shields and bags, mandalas, workbooks, consultations (tarot, etc.),
and a vast resource of knowledge.

# World Council Unity-and-Diversity

1010 S. Flower Street, #500, Los Angeles, CA 90015
(213) 742-6832

*Hours:* 10:00 a.m.–5:00 p.m., Monday–Friday
*Person to Contact:* Leland P. Stewart, Owner
*Founder/Owner:* Leland and Elizabeth Stewart (1965)
*Purpose:* A worldwide coordinating body of individuals, groups, and
    networks fostering new person and civilization.
*Facilities:* Center located at above address for meetings and programs.
    Offices and library.
*Services:* Health council, retreats, spiritual come-togethers, and other
    projects. Special AIDS workshop at UCLA. Other interesting heal-
    ing seminars, occasional retreats for unity-and-diversity training
    plus more general inner growth and meditation.
*Visions and Goals:* To help birth a new and global civilization based
    on unity-and-diversity.
*Materials Available:* Books for sale.


# Sweetwater Gardens Hot Tub & Sauna Spa

Box 377, 955 Ukiah Street, Mendocino, CA 95460
(707) 937-4140

*Hours:* 3:00 p.m.–10:00 p.m., Monday–Thursday; 12:00 a.m.–12:00
    p.m., Friday–Sunday
*Person to Contact:* Hawk or John, Owners
*Founder/Owner:* Hawk Kipnis and John Fliessback (1983)
*Purpose:* To improve health, restore mental balance through stress
    reduction and provide a nurturing social context for the entire com-
    munity.
*Facilities:* Three hot tubs, 2 saunas, 2 overnight rooms, Asian gift shop
    and natural juice bar.
*Services:* Lodging, tub and sauna rentals, massage (8 massage and body
    work practitioners working 3 hours), and counseling.
*Visions and Goals:* To promote health and well-being in a beautiful
    environment.
*Miscellaneous:* Fine redwood and stained-glass styling complement
    this unique spa. Private suites plus a large co-ed community tub and
    sauna. Water tower accommodations with ocean view. Friendly sup-
    portive staff.

# Harbin Hot Springs Retreat and Conference Center

P.O. Box 82, Middletown, CA 95461
(707) 987-2477; in California call (800) 622-2477

*Hours:* 7 days a week, 24 hours a day, 365 days a year

*Founder/Owner:* Ishvara (1971)

*Purpose:* To provide a serene, protective environment for relaxing, healing, and inspiration. To encourage personal expression, interpersonal relationship growth, and education in healthy physical, mental, and spiritual ways of living.

*Facilities:* Four guest houses, private rooms, dorms, and camping. Four workshop buildings—three with kitchen facilities, two with private warm pools. Hot, warm and cold mineral pools. Two Fire Circles and two Sweat Lodges. Community store, gift shop, and office store. Stonefront restaurant serving macrobiotic and natural breakfasts and dinners. Free movies every night in the theater. 1,160 acres for visioning and hiking.

*Services:* Workshops, which offer a safe place with qualified leaders to experiment with personal growth and transformation. Ongoing yoga, massage, and shiatsu classes, rebirthing, water shiatsu (Watsu) available daily. Nondenominational spiritual gatherings on Sundays.

*Visions and Goals:* To offer a supportive environment to accelerate personal and planetary healing.

*Materials Available:* CUS Community Store offers organic, natural, and bulk food items, vitamins, body care products and healthy snacks. Four Directions Gift Shop features crystals, healing stones, jewelry. Kachina dolls handmade by Zuni Indians, clothes and sachets. Office store carries New Age books and magazines, greeting cards, tapes, and tarot decks.

## Green Mountain Institute
20 Sheridan Court, Mill Valley, CA 94941
(415) 381-8763

*Hours:* 1:00 p.m.–10:00 pm, Tuesday–Sunday
*Person to Contact:* Robin Sierra, Director
*Founder/Owner:* Robin Sierra (Spring 1988)
*Purpose:* To be an inspiring and supportive space for people to safely explore and express their creative soul, in a contemplative and playful spirit.
*Facilities:* An art studio in a beautiful, quiet, and natural environment.
*Services:* Classes, workshops, and individual sessions in art, creative expression, and creative problem solving.
*Visions and Goals:* To be a vital force in the world which inspires people to open in a creative and compassionate way.

## The Institute for the Study of Natural Systems
P.O. Box 637, Mill Valley, CA 94942
(415) 383-5064

*Person to Contact:* James A. Swan, President
*Founder/Owner:* James A. Swan, Ph.D. (1987)
*Purpose:* To increase harmony between people and nature and encourage development of creative expression.
*Facilities:* A special middle school for the performing arts for creative and gifted children.
*Services:* Workshops and classes for adults and children.
*Visions and Goals:* To provide a summer camp to explore the creative and performing arts and how they are linked to nature. To expand our school, which has a strong root in nature, to provide for creative and gifted children from kindergarten age to 12 years old.
*Materials Available:* A catalog of books and tapes to promote harmony with nature.

# The Shakti (Gawain) Center

P.O. Box 377, Mill Valley, CA 94942
(415) 927-2277

*Hours:* 10:00 a.m.–3:00 p.m., Monday–Friday
*Founder/Owner:* Shakti Gawain (January 1987)
*Purpose:* Personal growth in all areas—emotional, spiritual, self-expression, creativity. Healing the emotions and helping people get in touch with their intuition. Self-expression is integrated into all programs through dance, movement, body, and art.
*Services:* Ongoing eight-week classes in a variety of subjects, including creative visualization, voice dialogue, support groups for emotional processing, African dance, drumming, and some channeling work. In addition, weekend workshops with guest leaders, Shakti Gawain, and private sessions with staff members.
*Visions and Goals:* Open the center up to more guest leaders.
*Materials Available:* Books and tapes.

# Center for Health and Well-Being

28892 Marguerite Parkway, #140, Mission Viejo, CA 92692
(714) 364-4434

*Hours:* 9:00 a.m.–7:00 p.m., Monday–Friday; 9:00 a.m. –12:00 noon, Saturday
*Person to Contact:* Robert or Holly Gahn
*Founder/Owner:* Robert R. Gahn, D.C., FIACA, and Holly A. Gahn, CA, OMD
*Purpose:* To open up new ideas, alternatives, and possibilities in overcoming various health problems and to assist in identifying and eliminating these causes of diseases.
*Facilities:* A healing center with a competent, energetic, and loving staff anxious to help in a warm, loving environment.
*Services:* Chiropractic, acupuncture, therapeutic massage, homeopathy, nutritional counseling, electrodiagnosis, herbology, iridology, Oriental medicine, and physical therapy.
*Visions and Goals:* To assist one in reaching their fullest potential—emotionally, chemically, structurally, energetically, and spiritually.
*Materials Available:* Books on health and body tools.

## The Light Blew Inn
200 Sheldon Avenue, #6, Mount Shasta, CA 96067
(916) 926-5653

*Hours:* Best time to call, before 7:00 a.m. or after 7:00 p.m., 7 days a
   week, May through September
*Person to Contact:* Danielle Light, Owner/Caretaker
*Founder/Owner:* Danielle Light (October 1985)
*Purpose:* To provide housing for open-minded individuals who live
   here year-round and a home away from home for those that want to
   visit and explore the power and beauty of Mount Shasta.
*Facilities:* Several cozy cabins within a peaceful garden courtyard. A
   fully equipped common kitchen, sundeck, and laundry facilities
   available for our guests.
*Services:* Accommodations include private and group rooms. Meals
   can be provided for workshops and classes. Information regarding
   the surrounding area and local healers, workshops, and activities.
*Visions and Goals:* To expand our network of "lightworkers" throughout the world.

## Murrieta Foundation
28779 Via Las Flores, Murrieta, CA 92362
(714) 677-9661

*Hours:* 8:00 a.m.–5:00 p.m., Monday–Friday; 9:00 a.m.–5:00 p.m.,
   Saturday and Sunday
*Person to Contact:* Barbara Maynard (best time, 9:00 a.m.–1:00 p.m.)
*Founder:* Barbara Maynard (1966)
*Purpose:* Murrieta Foundation is a nonprofit organization dedicated to
   healthful living. Murrieta programs teach a wholistic approach to
   health and fitness, personal growth, stress release, responsible and
   respectful relationships, and natural health techniques, specializing
   in polarity therapy.
*Facilities:* The resort's 47 acres provide a beautiful setting for comfortable lodging, full-range spa, healthy dining, and three outdoor mineral pools, 14 tennis courts, and an adjoining 18-hole golf course.
*Services:* Weekend seminars, one-week programs and four-week programs (both residential and program only). Programs entitled fit 'n
   trim, stress management, dynamic relationships awareness, body
   work, polarity therapy training.
*Visions and Goals:* Assist individuals in gaining optimum wellness
   through self-knowledge and personal responsibility.

## Las Brisas Retreat Center
43500 Camino de las Brisas, Murrieta, CA 92362
P.O. Box 500, Wildomar, CA 92395
(714) 499-5699 or (714) 742-7729

*Hours:* 7:00 a.m.–9:00 p.m., 7 days a week
*Founder/Owner:* Lee Coit (1983)
*Purpose:* To provide a quiet, supportive place for people to stay to refresh and renew their minds, bodies, and spirits. Each person is encouraged to follow his or her own inner guidance.
*Facilities:* More than 30 acres, 4,000 sq. ft. building, 6 bedrooms, library, meeting and meditation rooms, paths, nature walks, meditation spots, and spa, all in a remote natural setting with a contemplative atmosphere that offers many opportunities to enjoy nature.
*Services:* Workshops and seminars. Monthly "listening" seminars on how to increase awareness of your inner guide.
*Visions and Goals:* To maintain a quiet, naturally beautiful and supportive place for all to come and leave behind worldly distractions. Our vision is of a small community holding land in trust and supporting this concept.
*Materials Available:* Large book and tape library.

## Flower Essence Society /Earth-Spirit, Inc.

P.O. Box 459, Nevada City, CA 95959
(916) 265-9163

*Hours:* Flexible
*Person to Contact:* Patricia Kaminski, Educational Coordinator/
  Co-director
*Founder:* Richard Katz (1978)
*Owner:* Earth-Spirit, Inc., a nonprofit organization
*Purpose:* To sponsor a major summer retreat as well as other weekend
  retreats as announced. The purpose is to teach practical and inspira-
  tional knowledge about wildflowers and herbs.
*Facilities:* Located in the beautiful Sierra foothills of Nevada County.
  Our summer camp is just outside Nevada City and we take trips to
  other nearby locations. All meals are provided and private or group-
  style camping is available.
*Services:* Classes, weeklong intensives, practitioner training programs
  and membership programs. Richard Katz and Patricia Kaminski are
  the core faculty of the program, although other guest speakers are
  included.
*Visions and Goals:* To show that the outer world of nature is also an
  inner reality in our hearts.

## The Expanding Light

14618 Tyler Foote Road, Nevada City, CA 95959
(916) 292-3494

*Hours:* 9:00 a.m.–5:00 p.m., Monday–Saturday
*Person to Contact:* Richard McCord, Manager
*Founder/Owner:* Sri Kriyananda (1967)
*Purpose:* To provide techniques, support, and inspiration for personal
  spiritual growth in an atmosphere of joyful, healthful living. We are
  here to help the sincere spiritual seeker in every way we can.
*Facilities:* Accommodations include cabins and a dormitory clustered
  around a central building with dining room, temple, library, and
  lounge.
*Services:* Weekend, five-day, and four-week programs, flexible personal
  retreat and work/study programs, daily meditations and yoga, worship services, and evening programs. Classes, personal counseling,
  delicious vegetarian meals, and outings in the beautiful Sierra
  Nevada mountains.
*Visions and Goals:* As our founder once said, "We're not here to make
  sick people well. We're here to make well people better."

## The Institute for the Development of the Harmonious Human Being, Inc.

P.O. Box 370, Nevada City, CA 95959
(916) 477-1116

*Hours:* 8:00 a.m.–7:00 p.m., Monday–Friday
*Person to Contact:* Ann-Victoria Hopcroft, J.D.
*Founder/Owner:* Nonprofit, incorporated in 1973
*Purpose:* Service to the Absolute, especially providing resources and artifacts for those awakening to service now and in the future.
*Facilities:* Operates primarily as a resource and consultation center by correspondence.
*Services:* Projects include Gateways books and tapes, Heidelberg Editions International, Labyrinth Readers Course, Academy of Ancient Arts, and Alchemical Gold Essential Oils.
*Visions and Goals:* The institute advocates "work on self" toward awakening to the path of service in everyday life. It offers resources and assistance to individuals seriously motivated to go beyond study and apply transformative ideas in their lives, making a place for the Great Work in their lives.
*Materials Available:* Catalog for introductory books and cassettes.

## Inner Light Foundation

P.O. Box 761, Novato, CA 94948
(415) 382-1040

*Hours:* 9:30 a.m.–4:30 p.m., Monday–Friday
*Person to Contact:* Marynell Tipton, Office Manager
*Founder:* Betty Bethards (1967)
*Owner:* Nonprofit foundation
*Purpose:* A spiritual, educational, and nondenominational foundation that offers ongoing programs in understanding the human potential and teaching a free meditation technique, how to work with dreams and affirmations, and visualization to all who wish to learn.
*Facilities:* We have an office in the San Francisco Bay area and five monthly lectures in the Bay area and Los Angeles.
*Services:* We offer a free newsletter and teach a powerful meditation technique at no charge as well as classes/lectures and personal readings.
*Visions and Goals:* To encourage all persons to practice the law of love in their daily lives and to live in harmony and balance.
*Materials Available:* Books by Betty Berthards, including her best-selling *The Dream Book*, lecture tapes, meditation music tapes, and guided imagery tapes by Dr. Cary Howard.

## The Center of Artistic Counseling
5425 College Avenue, #2, Oakland, CA 94618
(415) 654-4462

*Person to Contact:* Margret Elson, Director
*Founder/Owner:* Margret Elson (1983)
*Purpose:* To help artists in all fields—as well as anyone involved in creative endeavors—solve any difficulties of an emotional or artistic nature which may arise. Problems associated with entering the creative arena, developing artistic vision, and realizing artistic goals are addressed.
*Facilities:* Individual and small group work is done at the Center of Artistic Counseling. Other locations for large groups and lectures.
*Services:* Individual sessions, usually short-term and goal oriented, workshops, lectures. Workshops designed especially for musicians, students, their parents, teachers, teen-age and adult students. Consultations for teachers experiencing difficulty with particular students. Business presentations to increase on-the-job creativity.
*Visions and Goals:* To provide a place for artists to congregate, discuss their work, and find help with the problems they encounter.

## Iyengar Yoga in Ojai Valley/Ojai Yoga Center
203 N. Signal Street, Ojai, CA 93023
(805) 640-0448

*Hours:* 24 hours a day, 7 days a week
*Person to Contact:* Judi Flannery or Suza Francina
*Founder/Owner:* Judi Flannery and Suza Francina (September 1986)
*Purpose:* To offer yoga classes in the Iyengar tradition to beginning and intermediate students.
*Facilities:* Fully equipped Iyengar yoga studio. Access to mineral hot springs and hiking.
*Services:* Daily yoga classes with certified Iyengar yoga teachers, group and private lessons, weekend workshops.
*Visions and Goals:* To provide yoga intensives and retreats for out-of-town students, and workshops with guest teachers.
*Materials Available:* All yoga props including back benders and pelvic strings as well as books on yoga.

# Vega Study Center

1511 Robinson Street, Oroville, CA 95965
(916) 533-7702

*Hours:* 9 a.m.–5 p.m., Monday–Friday
*Person to Contact:* Carl Ferré, Business Manager
*Founder:* Herman and Cornellia Aihara (1974)
*Owner:* Nonprofit corporation
*Purpose:* To provide an environment where participants can become
acquainted with macrobiotic information, philosophy, and skills
they can use to improve their physical, emotional, and spiritual
well-being.
*Facilities:* Forty-six rooms, 13,000-square-foot building in downtown
Oroville. Two saunas, private and shared rooms. Store with natural
products and books.
*Services:* Two week live-in study program, weekend workshops, private consultations with Herman Aihara, and annual summer camp
in late July at French Meadows in the Tahoe National Forest.
*Visions and Goals:* To enhance the health of each individual, thus
affecting the vision of the nation and elevating the consciousness of
the world.
*Miscellaneous:* Couples and group rates available.

# Movement Expression

622 Las Lomas Avenue, Pacific Palisades, CA 90272
(213) 454-5335

*Hours:* 9:00 a.m.–6:00 p.m., Monday–Friday
*Person to Contact:* Eve Athey Ray or Mariane Athey Karou
*Founder/Owners:* Eve Athery Ray and Mariane Athey Karou (1976)
*Purpose:* To provide classes and workshops for individuals to express
themselves more fully and freely, to trust themselves more deeply,
and to have fun in a safe supportive environment. Movement Expression combines movement and guided imagery into a series of
unique exercises that help one to open up, let go, and become free
and comfortable with oneself and others. Moving to the rhythms of
primitive, classical, and popular music, Movement Expression is a
fun way to get great exercise while becoming more self-confident
and increasing self-awareness.
*Facilities:* Studio. (Classes are held at Yoga Works, 1426 Montana Ave.,
Santa Monica, on the 2nd floor).
*Services:* Workshops, classes, private sessions, and video work.

## Shenoa Retreat Center

P.O. Box 43, Philo, CA 95466
(707) 895-3156

*Hours:* 9:00 a.m.–6:30 p.m., Monday–Friday
*Person to Contact:* Stephan Brown, Director
*Purpose:* Grown from a small circle of former Findhorn Community members to a larger network of friends and supporters on the Pacific Coast, Shenoa Retreat Center is located in a beautiful, calm setting where people can gather for renewal and inspiration to reflect and interact with other like-minded and like-hearted people.
*Facilities:* Eighteen cabins or rooms, the majority of which have their own private bathroom. Cabins that accommodate up to 65 people for group gatherings such as weddings, reunions, seminars, workshops, or meetings. Camping is available for 50 or more people. Dining lodge seats 100. Swimming pool and river. Facilities for playing tennis, basketball, volleyball, and badminton.
*Services:* Three excellent vegetarian meals served daily. Shenoa's staff and invited faculty periodically present events, programs, and gatherings. An educational environment working with gardening and cooperation with nature, group dynamics, personal integration and meditation.

## Association for Past-Life Research and Therapy

P.O. Box 20151, Riverside, CA 92516
(714) 784-1570

*Hours:* 9:30 a.m.–5:00 p.m., Monday–Friday
*Person to Contact:* Hazel M. Henning, Ph.D., Executive Director
*Founded:* October 1980
*Owner:* Nonprofit corporation; Trisha Caetano, President
*Purpose:* To direct effective treatment so individuals become aware of their capacity to improve their lives, physical or psychological. To coordinate networking of members, sending referral lists to those who request a therapist in their area.
*Facilities:* A suite of six offices, a large meeting room, and a library shared with the Parapsychology Association of Riverside.
*Services:* Twice yearly conferences, twice yearly training workshops for therapists, and 3 to 6 seminars a year on various subjects including birth trauma, holographic imaging, and clinical depossession.
*Visions and Goals:* The dream is a disease-free society, at ease in body and mind, paying attention to the Karmic connection in all life.
*Materials Available:* Journal and Newsletter.

# Journeys into the Known

P.O. Box 7422, San Diego, CA 92107
(619) 222-0904

*Hours:* 10:00 a.m.–3:00 p.m.
*Person to Contact:* Billie C. Delawie
*Founder/Owner:* Billie C. Delawie, Ph.D. (1984)
*Purpose:* To provide opportunities all too rare in our lives: a safe time, place, and perspective in which to both share pieces of our stories and release the burden of loneliness and fear that we seem to carry in our cells.
*Services:* Programs offered regularly in San Diego, California, through workshops, medicine wheels, classes, and weekend retreats. Individual integrative sessions offered using Motherpeace tarot and runes. Consultant in conference planning.
*Programs offered include:*
Journeys into the Known, which presents a variety of programs created in recognition of the myriad ways that the Greater Reality calls us in daily life. Each moment, each event is a spiritual journey if we are but willing to know it.
Sacred Circles: Empowering the Feminine, which uses the Wisdom of the Wheel for self-insight and creating bonded communities.
Healing the Masculine, which seeks to identify and heal the father-daughter wound.
Embracing the Feminine, which aims to empower the Feminine through opening up the mother/daughter relationship to new understanding.
The Wealth of Maturity, which enables us to claim our Wise Inner Woman and bring her into a world that needs her wisdom sorely.
Divorce as Spirit Calling, which goes beyond the pain and struggle to find meaning in the larger journey.
Womanquest, Feminine Paths to Spirituality, which uses myth, the arts, psychology, ritual and ceremonies seeking to invoke the authentic Feminine voice within.
*Visions and Goals:* To expand our programs farther afield.

# Earth Children

3817 Ray Street, San Diego, CA 92104
(619) 296-4476

*Hours:* 10:00 a.m.–6:00 p.m., Tuesday–Saturday
*Person to Contact:* Jenny Star
*Founder/Owner:* Jenny Star (June 1986)
*Purpose:* To provide an alternative atmosphere where New Age thinking people can meet, grow, and support one another.
*Facilities:* Store, classroom and library.
*Services:* Crystal healing, Reiki healing, counseling, psychic readings, workshops, lectures, custom work, channeled work, networking, bartering, presentations, and classes on dance, yoga, and health. We also take on consignment and promote local craftspeople and creative people.
*Visions and Goals:* An enlightenment center with alternative paths for mental, emotional, physical, and spiritual needs to increase the networking, information, and classes.
*Materials Available:* Over 2,500 books, the largest selection of gemstones and crystals in the area, tapes, videos, and musical instruments.

# The Healing Center of San Francisco

(a.k.a. Nurse Consultants and Health Counselors)
465 Brussels Street, San Francisco, CA 94134
(415) 468-4680

*Hours:* 8:00 a.m.–8:00 p.m., Monday–Friday
*Person to Contact:* Jocelyne M. Nielsen
*Founder/Owner:* Jocelyne M. Nielsen (1973)
*Purpose:* Education and healing through classes, meditations, treatments, and consultations. Model of private practice for nurses.
*Facilities:* Large two-story house with garden open for people to come to meditate, use the library, "be" in the garden, and purchase food and supplements in our small store.
*Services:* Treatments by appointment: reading, counseling, massage, acupressure, therapeutic touch, hypnosis, and so forth.
*Visions and Goals:* To be a center of light in the city environment. To provide health care and education to develop spiritual awareness and a spiritual practice with people interested in doing it with us. To form a community and continue sharing our gifts and resources with each other.
*Materials Available:* Library open for anyone who wishes to consult books and current information.

# Min An Health Center

1144 Pacific Avenue, San Francisco, CA 94133
(415) 771-4040

*Hours:* 9:00 a.m.–6:00 p.m., Monday–Friday
*Person to Contact:* Wendy Buffet
*Founder:* Hanmin Liv (1980)
*Owner:* Nonprofit
*Purpose:* To provide quality health care that integrates both Western
and traditional Chinese medical health practices.
*Facilities:* Two medical offices, a dental office, and an acupuncturist's
office.
*Services:* Office gynecology, primary care, acupuncture, nutritional
counseling, dentistry, and psychotherapy.
*Visions and Goals:* To promote high-level wellness in the community.

# The Spiritual Healing Center

1739 Anza Street, San Francisco, CA 94118
(415) 221-4058

*Hours:* 1:00 p.m.–6:00 p.m., Monday–Friday
*Person to Contact:* Sophia Tiers
*Founder/Owner:* Rev. Joseph Martinez (January 1979)
*Purpose:* Spiritual healing, transformation of consciousness, and the
practice of the integral yoga of Sri Aurobindo.
*Facilities:* Healing room and meditation room.
*Services:* Regular meetings include prayer service and dental healing,
meditation and healing. Spiritual healing, counseling and polarity
therapy are offered periodically. All teachings represent a combina-
tion of esoteric, metaphysics, Christianity, and Eastern religions,
with a special emphasis on the integral yoga of Sri Aurobindo.
*Visions and Goals:* Personal and global healing, transformation practice, and completion of integral yoga.
*Materials Available:* In-house library, small bookstore, and massage
tables.
*Miscellaneous:* Rev. Martinez is a full-time healer from the Philippines and vice-president, in the United States, of the Philippines
Healers Circle.

# New Dimensions Radio

P.O. Box 410510, San Francisco, CA 94141
(415) 563-8899

*Person to Contact:* Michael Toms, Host
*Founder:* New Dimensions Foundation (March 1973)
*Owner:* Public, nonprofit educational organization
*Purpose:* A listener-sponsored program, New Dimensions Radio provides
  a viable alternative to the mainstream media where negative news
  and what's wrong with the world are so often emphasized. Through
  the nationally syndicated "New Dimensions" radio series and tapes,
  you can listen to the myriad ways in which human society is changing for the better, the abundant possibilities for celebrating life in all
  its fullness, and how together we can create a world that works for
  everybody. "New Dimensions" has been called the "Whole Earth
  Catalog of the Air" because of its breadth of vision and depth of
  insight.
*Services:* Nationally recognized as a unique and professional production, New Dimensions Radio programming has featured hundreds of
  the most profound thinkers of our time in far-ranging dialogues
  covering the major issues of this era. Some examples are The Path of
  Partnership with Hugh and Gayle Prather; Into the Deep: Male Mys-
  teries with Robert Bly; Call of the Hero with Joseph Campbell; Say
  "Yes" to Love with Leo Buscaglia; Helping Yourself with Ram Dass;
  Transforming Your Life with Shakti Gawain; Transformation in
  Health with Brugh Joy and Richard Moss; Fire Spirit with Lynn
  Andrews; Becoming Whole with Virginia Satir and The Heart of
  Healing with Stephen Levine. A membership program called
  Friends of New Dimensions offers each member a 15 percent dis-
  count on all tape and book purchases, invitations to special events,
  and a copy of the New Dimensions Radio Network News newsletter.
*Materials Available:* New Dimensions Newsletter, published
  bimonthly. Books and New Dimensions tapes; some of the best and
  brightest visions that have been heard on the "New Dimensions"
  radio interview series.
*Miscellaneous:* For a free copy of the New Dimensions Newsletter and
  a list of the most popular tapes write: New Dimensions Radio, Dept.
  JM, P.O. Box 410510, San Francisco, CA 94141.

# THE RADIO NETWORK

| City | Station | Freq. | Day | Time |
|---|---|---|---|---|
| Huntsville, AL | WLRH-FM | 89.3 | MON | 10:00 PM |
| Big Lake/Anchorage, AK | KABN-AM | 830 | SUN | 6:00 PM |
| Craig, AK | KRBD-FM | 101.7 | WED | 7:00 PM |
| Haines, AK | KHNS-FM | 102.3 | SUN | 9:30 AM |
| Homer, AK | KBBI-AM | 890 | SUN | 7:00 PM |
| Hydaburg,AK | KRBD-FM | 90.1 | WED | 7:00 PM |
| Ketchikan, AK | KRBD-FM | 105.9 | WED | 7:00 PM |
| Klawock, AK | KRBD-FM | 90.1 | WED | 7:00 PM |
| Mountain Point, AK | KRBD-FM | 90.1 | WED | 7:00 PM |
| Thorne Bay/Hollis, AK | KRBD-FM | 90.1 | WED | 7:00 PM |
| Little Rock, AR | KABF-FM | 88.3 | FRI | 9:00 AM |
| Tucson, AZ | KXCI-FM | 91.7 | SUN | 11:00 PM |
| Arcata, CA | KHSU-FM | 90.5 | SUN | 10:00 PM |
| Berkeley, CA | KBLX-AM | 1400 | SUN | 7:00 AM * |
| Berkeley, CA | KBLX-FM | 102.9 | SUN | 7:00 AM * |
| Crescent City, CA | KSOR-FM | 91.7 | SUN | 4:00 PM |
| Garberville, CA | KMUD-FM | 91.1 | MON | 8:00 PM |
| Mendocino/Ft. Bragg, CA | KLLK-CABLE | 101.9 | SUN | 9:00 PM + |
| Mt. Shasta/McCloud, CA | KSOR-FM | 88.3 | SUN | 4:00 PM |
| Pacific Grove, CA | KAZU-FM | 90.3 | SUN | 9:00 PM |
| Redlands, CA | KUOR-FM | 89.1 | WED | 8:00 PM |
| Redwood Valley, CA | KLLK-CABLE | 101.9 | SUN | 9:00 PM + |
| Rohnert Park, CA | KSUN-CABLE | 91.1 | SAT | 5:00 PM |
|  |  |  | SUN | 5:00 PM |
| San Francisco, CA | KALW-FM | 91.7 | SUN | 11:00 PM |
| San Francisco, CA | KOIT-AM | 1260 | SUN | 3:00 AM |
|  |  |  | MON | 12:00 AM |
| San Francisco, CA | KOIT-FM | 96.5 | SUN | 3:00 AM |
| Santa Cruz, CA | KZSC-FM | 88.1 | TUE | 7:30 AM |
| Ukiah, CA | KLLK-CABLE | 101.9 | SUN | 9:00 PM + |
| Weed, CA | KSOR-FM | 89.5 | SUN | 4:00 PM |
| Yreka/Montague, CA | KSOR-FM | 91.5 | SUN | 4:00 PM |
| Willits, CA | KLLK-AM | 1250 | SUN | 9:00 PM |
| Willits, CA | KLLK-CABLE | 101.9 | SUN | 9:00 PM + |
| Aspen, CO | KDNK-FM | 88.3 | WED | NOON |
|  |  |  | SUN | 6:30 PM |
| Aspen, CO | KUNC-FM | 90.9 | SUN | 7:00 PM |
| Basalt, CO | KDNK-FM | 88.3 | WED | NOON |
|  |  |  | SUN | 6:30 PM |
| Carbondale, CO | KDNK-FM | 90.5 | WED | NOON |
|  |  |  | SUN | 6:30 PM |
| Estes Park, CO | KUNC-FM | 90.9 | SUN | 7:00 PM |
| Fort Collins, CO | KUNC-FM | 91.5 | SUN | 7:00 PM |
| Glenwood Springs, CO | KDNK-FM | 91.3 | THU | NOON |
| Greeley, CO | KUNC-FM | 91.5 | SUN | 7:00 PM |
| Gypsum/Eagle Valley, CO | KUNC-FM | 88.7 | SUN | 7:00 PM |
| Marble, CO | KDNK-FM | 88.3 | WED | NOON |
|  |  |  | SUN | 6:30 PM |
| Paonia, CO | KVNF-FM | 90.9 | THU | NOON |
| Snowmass, CO | KDNK-FM | 88.3 | WED | NOON |
|  |  |  | SUN | 6:30 PM |
| Steamboat Springs, CO | KUNC-FM | 90.7 | SUN | 7:00 PM |
| Sterling, CO | KUNC-FM | 90.9 | SUN | 7:00 PM |
| Vail, CO | KUNC-FM | 88.7 | SUN | 7:00 PM |
| Storrs, CT | WHUS-FM | 91.7 | TUE | 6:00 PM |
|  |  |  | FRI | 9:00 AM |
| Newark, DE | WXDR-FM | 91.3 | THU | 2:00 PM |
| Miami, FL | WXDJ-FM | 95.7 | SUN | 7:00 AM |
|  |  |  | MON | 1:00 AM |
| Panama City, FL | WKGC-AM | 1480 | MON | 6:00 PM |
| Atlanta, GA | WRAS-FM | 88.5 | FRI | 5:00 AM |
| Boise, ID | KBSU-FM | 91.3 | SUN | 9:00 PM |
| Chicago, IL | WBEZ-FM | 91.5 | TUE | 7:00 PM |
| Elmhurst, IL | WRSE-FM | 88.7 | TUE | 12:30 PM |
| Glen Ellyn, IL | WDCB-FM | 90.9 | MON | 10:00 PM |
| Summit, IL | WARG-FM | 88.9 | FRI | 9:00 AM |
| Urbana, IL | WILL-AM | 580 | SAT | 5:00 PM ** |
| Columbia City, IN | WJHS-FM | 91.5 | MON | 9:00 AM |
|  |  |  | FRI | 1:00 PM |
| Indianapolis, IN | WICR-FM | 88.7 | MON | 3:00 PM |
| South Bend, IN | WETL-FM | 91.7 | WED | 3:30 PM |
| Iowa City, IA | WSUI-AM | 910 | THU | 2:15 PM |
|  |  |  | SAT | 2:00 PM |
| Wichita, KS | KLZS-FM | 97.9 | SUN | 6:00 AM |
| Louisville, KY | WFPL-FM | 89.3 | MON | 11:30 AM |
| Newport/Highland Heights, KY | WNKU-FM | 89.7 | THU | 9:00 AM |
|  |  |  | SUN | 11:00 PM |
| Whitesburg, KY | WMMT-FM | 88.7 | SUN | 10:30 AM |
| West Barnstable, MA | WKKL-FM | 89.7 | WED | 12:30 PM |
| Frostburg, MD | WFWM-FM | 91.7 | SAT | 10:00 AM |
| Princess Anne, MD | WESM-FM | 91.3 | MON | 7:00 PM |
|  |  |  | TUE | 9:00 AM |
| Blue Hill Falls, ME | WERU-FM | 89.9 | MON | 10:00 AM |
| Gorham, ME | WMPG-FM | 90.9 | SAT | NOON |
| Alpena, MI | WCML-FM | 91.7 | SUN | 7:00 PM |
| Ann Arbor, MI | WUOM-FM | 91.7 | SUN | 9:00 AM |
| Detroit, MI | WDTR-FM | 90.9 | TUE | 12:30 PM |
|  |  |  | THU | 4:30 PM |
| Flint, MI | WFUM-FM | 91.1 | SUN | 7:00 PM |
| Grand Rapids, MI | WVGR-FM | 104.1 | SUN | 7:00 PM |
| Mt. Pleasant, MI | WCMU-FM | 89.5 | SUN | 7:00 PM |
| Duluth, MN | KUMD-FM | 103.3 | SUN | 9:00 PM |
| Glenwood, MN | KZZA-FM | 107.1 | SUN | 11:00 AM |
| Grand Rapids, MN | KAXE-FM | 91.7 | MON | NOON |
|  |  |  | WED | 9:00 PM |
| Minneapolis, MN | KBEM-FM | 88.5 | SUN | 2:00 PM |
|  |  |  | WED | 11:00 PM |
| Columbia, MO | KOPN-FM | 89.5 | WED | 7:00 PM |
| Kansas City, MO | KCUR-FM | 89.3 | SAT | 6:00 AM |
| Pt. Lookout, MO | KSOZ-FM | 91.7 | WED | 12:30 PM |
| Bozeman, MT | KGLT-FM | 91.9 | SUN | 10:05 PM |
| Butte, MT | KUFM-FM | 99.3 | THU | 9:30 PM |
| Great Falls, MT | KGPR-FM | 89.9 | THU | 9:30 PM |
| Helena, MT | KUFM-FM | 107.1 | THU | 9:30 PM |
| Missoula, MT | KUFM-FM | 89.1 | THU | 9:30 PM |
| White Sulphur Springs, MT | KGPR-FM | 98.3 | THU | 9:30 PM |
| Buies Creek, NC | WCCE-FM | 90.1 | TUE | 8:30 PM |
| Lincoln, NE | KZUM-FM | 89.3 | SAT | 9:00 AM |
| Las Cruces, NM | KRWG-FM | 90.7 | SUN | 7:00 PM |
| Santa Fe, NM | KMIK-AM | 810 | SUN | 7:00 AM |
| Brockport/Rochester, NY | WBSU-FM | 88.9 | MON | 4:00 PM |
|  |  |  | THU | 9:00 AM |
| Fredonia, NY | WCVF-FM | 88.9 | FRI | 1:00 PM |
| Geneva, NY | WEOS-FM | 89.7 | WED | 6:00 PM |
| Hempstead, NY | WRHU-FM | 88.7 | WED | 8:00 PM |
| New York, NY | WNYC-AM | 830 | SUN | 6:00 PM |
| Stony Brook, NY | WUSB-FM | 90.1 | FRI | 10:00 AM |
| Troy, NY | WRPI-FM | 91.5 | SUN | 10:00 PM |
| Fargo, ND | KDSU-FM | 91.9 | SAT | 3:00 PM |
| Akron, OH | WAPS-FM | 89.1 | THU | 10:00 AM |
| Cincinnati, OH | WNKU-FM | 89.7 | THU | 9:00 AM |
|  |  |  | SUN | 11:00 PM |
| Cleveland, OH | WUJC-FM | 88.7 | TUE | 9:00 PM |
| Hamilton, OH | WHSS-FM | 89.5 |  | Call Station |
| Yellow Springs, OH | WYSO-FM | 91.3 | FRI | 1:00 PM |
| Ashland, OH | KSOR-FM | 90.1 | SUN | 4:00 PM |
| Bend, OR | KLCC-FM | 91.5 | SAT | 9:00 AM |
| Bend, OR | KOAB-FM | 91.3 | SUN | 2:00 PM |
| Coos Bay/North Bend, OR | KSOR-FM | 89.1 | SUN | 4:00 PM |
| Cottage Grove, OR | KLCC-FM | 91.5 | SAT | 9:00 AM |
| Corvallis, OR | KOAC-AM | 550 | SUN | 2:00 PM |
| Eugene, OR | KLCC-FM | 89.7 | SAT | 9:00 AM |
| Florence, OR | KLCC-FM | 92.7 | SAT | 9:00 AM |
| Grants Pass, OR | KSOR-FM | 88.9 | SUN | 4:00 PM |
| Klamath Falls, OR | KSOR-FM | 90.5 | SUN | 4:00 PM |
| Medford, OR | KSOR-FM | 90.1 | SUN | 4:00 PM |
| Medford/Ashland, OR | KSMF-FM | 89.1 | SUN | 4:00 PM |
| Newport/Lincoln City, OR | KLCC-FM | 88.9 | SAT | 9:00 AM |
| Oakridge, OR | KLCC-FM | 91.5 | SAT | 9:00 AM |
| Pendleton, OR | KRBM-FM | 90.9 | SUN | 2:00 PM |
| Portland, OR | KOAP-FM | 91.5 | SUN | 2:00 PM |
| Port Orford, OR | KSOR-FM | 90.5 | SUN | 4:00 PM |
| Roseburg, OR | KSOR-FM | 90.5 | SUN | 4:00 PM |
| Erie, PA | WQLN-FM | 91.3 | MON | 1:00 PM |
| Chattanooga, TN | WUTC-FM | 88.1 | SUN | 1:00 PM |
| Johnson City, TN | WETS-FM | 89.5 | SAT | 9:00 PM |
| Knoxville, TN | WUOT-FM | 91.9 | SUN | 1:00 PM |
| Memphis, TN | WQOX-FM | 88.5 | MON | 8:30 AM |
|  |  |  | FRI | 8:30 AM |
| Nashville, TN | WFSK-FM | 88.1 |  | Call Station |
| Austin, TX | KBTS-FM | 93.3 | SUN | 7:00 AM |
| Austin, TX | KUT-FM | 90.5 | SUN | 4:00 PM |
| Conroe, TX | KPHD-FM | 1140 | TUE | 5:00 PM |
| El Paso, TX | KTEP-FM | 88.5 | SAT | 9:00 AM |
| Ft. Worth, TX | KTCU-FM | 88.7 | SAT | 6:00 PM |
| Houston, TX | KPFT-FM | 90.1 | MON | 11:00 AM |
| San Antonio, TX | KSYM-FM | 90.1 |  | Call Station |
| Salt Lake City, UT | KRCL-FM | 90.9 | SUN | 9:00 PM |
|  |  |  | THU | 1:00 PM |
| Burlington, VT | WVPS-FM | 107.9 | SUN | 10:00 PM |
| Windsor, VT | WVPR-FM | 89.5 | SUN | 10:00 PM |
| Lexington, VA | WLUR-FM | 91.5 | THU | 8:00 PM |
| Roanoke, VA | WVTF-FM | 89.1 | FRI | 7:00 PM |
| Bellevue, WA | KBCS-FM | 91.2 | THU | 7:00 PM |
| Bellingham, WA | KUGS-FM | 89.3 | FRI | 10:00 AM |
| Pullman, WA | KZUU-FM | 90.7 |  | Call Station |
| Tacoma/Seattle, WA | KTPS-FM | 91.7 | MON | 6:30 PM |
| Appleton, WI | WLFM-FM | 91.1 | THU | 7:30 PM |
| Burlington, WI | WBSD-FM | 89.1 | WED | 10:00 PM |
| Hayward, WI | WOJB-FM | 88.9 | SUN | 8:00 AM |
| La Crosse, WI | WLSU-FM | 88.9 | SUN | 7:00 PM |
|  |  |  | WED | 10:00 AM |
| Madison, WI | WORT-FM | 89.9 | TUE | 1:00 PM |
| Milwaukee, WI | WYMS-FM | 88.9 | SAT | 8:00 AM |
|  |  |  | SUN | 7:00 PM |
| Cheyenne, WY | KUNC-FM | 91.5 | SUN | 7:00 PM |

**WILL-AM—Urbana, IL:
—Airs the second and fourth Saturdays of month only.

# Red Victorian Bed and Breakfast Inn/Global Family Networking Center

1665 Haight Street, San Francisco, CA 94117
(415) 864-1978

*Hours:* 8:30 a.m.–10:00 p.m., Thursday–Tuesday (until 7:30 p.m. Wednesday)

*Person to Contact:* Haven Trevino, Manager

*Founder/Owner:* Sami Sunchild (1978)

*Purpose:* The world's first Global Family Bed and Breakfast Network Center. The purpose of the Global Family is the shifting of mass consciousness from fear and separation to unity and love, as predicted by the flower children. The Red Victorian offers a peaceful haven in the heart of the bustling city and provides a caring, home-away-from-home for globally conscious travelers.

*Facilities:* Fifteen unique rooms, inspired by themes of Golden Gate Park and the Flower Child era. Guests may choose from the Butterfly Room, the Japanese Tea Garden Room, the Redwood Forest Room, the Sunshine Room, the Teddy Bear Room, the Peacock Palace Suite, and others. The Peace Gallery of transformational, calligraphic art is the setting for seminars, meetings, and weddings. Meditation Room and Pink Parlour.

*Services:* New Age hotel, continental breakfast served. Therapeutic massage and meditation. Information and education services related to world peace, natural healing, and personal growth. Global Family open house meetings are held regularly. Two-month, intensive and personalized Global Family Bed and Breakfast Center planning and hospitality trainings are offered on location in San Francisco. Also three-day introductory meeting, "Is There a Global Family Bed and Breakfast Center in my Future?"

*Visions and Goals:* Sami Sunchild and her Developmental Management Team hold a vision of Global Family Bed and Breakfast Centers in gateway cities around the world. Initial cities targeted include Moscow, London, Tokyo, New York, Boston, Washington, D.C., Los Angeles, Seattle, Honolulu, Toronto, Vancouver, Auckland, and Sydney, among others. Each location will reflect not a cookie cutter, multinational hotel-chain image but a distinctly local flavor offering guests an experience of each community's culture.

*Materials Available:* Transformational art for sale, books, tapes (including tapes on cancer self-healing), and gifts.

# Sunrise Center, Inc. (Celebrations of Love)

1452 8th Avenue, San Francisco, CA 94122
(415) 661-8671

*Person to Contact:* Shoshana, Office Manager
*Founder/Owner:* Lori Grace (1976)
*Purpose:* To provide a series of weekend and weeklong retreats and one-day workshops in Tantra Yoga. Tantra teaches us to embrace all that life has to offer rather than to resist it. It is also known as the Yoga of Intimacy and Sexuality. Our staff are highly qualified professionals in various forms of psychological therapies, body work, movement, music, and Tantra Yoga.
*Facilities:* Retreats and workshops are held at two different locations: Hale Akua (Home of the Divine) in Maui, Hawaii, a totally private fantasy garden estate, and Harbin Hot Springs, two and a half hours north of San Francisco, California, a beautiful mountain retreat center. Lori Grace's home in beautiful Tiburon, California, is used for follow-up evenings.
*Services:* Celebrations of Love Workshops/Retreats: Journey into Love, our 7- to 10-day retreat in Hawaii; Opening into Love, our two and a half to three and a half day retreat in California; and Advanced Tantra Workshop, our 4- to 5-day retreat in Hawaii.

# Transformative Arts Institute

P.O. Box 387, San Geronimo, CA 94963
(415) 488-4965

*Hours:* 11:00 a.m.–7:00 p.m., Monday–Friday
*Person to Contact:* Richard Dobson or Natasha Frazier, Directors
*Founder/Owner:* Richard Dobson and Natasha Frazier (1983)
*Purpose:* Education, facilitation, and research into the arts of shamanic power, healing, and knowledge and their integration in a contemporary life path. It serves as a "home base" for everything from information and individual counseling to highly structured group processes and trainings.
*Facilities:* Dorm-style accommodations, camping, spa/sauna, and trading post.
*Services:* Experiential one-day and weekend retreats. Yearlong training; apprentice and group work, 100-hour Ericksonian practitioner and 150-hour hypnotherapist certification; sacred crafts; counseling in change work, spiritual preparation, and developing inner resources.
*Visions and Goals:* Residential and retreat programs for Vietnam veterans, children, and teens.

# Intuitive Development Institute

17 El Cerrito Avenue, San Rafael, CA 94901
(415) 454-3477

*Hours:* 9:00 a.m.–5:00 p.m., Monday–Friday
*Person to Contact:* Susan Stuart-Patton, Director
*Founder/Owner:* Susan Stuart-Patton, Ph.D. (1981)
*Purpose:* The institute was established to promote the expansion of intuitive awareness, psychic abilities, and spiritual healing.
*Facilities:* One-third acre in central Marin County with lovely space for classes and workshops and an office in Carmel Valley.
*Services:* The institute offers psychic readings, intuitive counseling, past life workshops, public lectures, and intuitive classes and seminars.
*Visions and Goals:* To not only develop one's intuition but to put it to use on a daily basis, to find the perfect relationship, the right career, the highest yielding financial investment, or the most expansive spiritual connection.
*Materials Available:* Audiocassette tapes of lectures and classes.
*Miscellaneous:* Intuitive counseling is ongoing; private sessions to remove emotional blocks to awareness and to develop and expand one's intuitive ability.

# White Lotus Foundation
2500 San Marcos Pass, Santa Barbara, CA 93105
(805) 964-1944

*Hours:* 8:30 a.m.–7:00 p.m., 7 days a week
*Person to Contact:* Tracey Rich, Associate Director
*Founder:* Ganga White (1967)
*Owner:* WLF, nonprofit
*Purpose:* An oasis for learning teachings of yoga and contemporary and ancient wisdom in a beautiful natural setting.
*Facilities:* Forty-acre mountain center overlooking the city and ocean. Yurts, indoor accommodations and forested, plateau, or creekside campsites. Main facilities are a large yoga meeting room, kitchen and dining room serving organic vegetarian meals, living room/library media center, and bookstore.
*Services:* Weekend, seven-day and sixteen-day in-depth yoga training courses, teacher certification, weekly Hatha yoga classes and personal retreats.
*Materials Available:* Books, tapes, and Hatha yoga tools.


# Hay Institute
P.O. Box 2212, Santa Monica, CA 90406
(213) 394-7445

*Hours:* 9:00 a.m.–5:30 p.m., Monday–Friday
*Person to Contact:* Jim Smith or John Gatzemeier
*Founder/Owner:* Louise L. Hay
*Purpose:* "Creating a world where it is safe for us to love others." Based on the philosophy of her book *You Can Heal Your Life,* the Hay Institute is the educational arm of Louise L. Hay's work.
*Services:* We sponsor workshops and lectures and produce the annual Intensive Training Program and other support groups. We have also established an international network of healing circles, many of which specifically address AIDS. If you would like information on specific cities, please call the institute.
*Miscellaneous:* Because of her incredible success and the demands on her time Louise has decided to no longer facilitate workshops. She will personally concentrate on lectures. The Institute is preparing to make Louise's "Love Yourself—Heal Your Life" workshop available to sponsors in 1989. They will be facilitated by associate teachers who have been hand picked and trained by Louise. If you are interested in being a sponsor, please call us.

# Santa Monica Healing Arts Center

1453 7th Street, Santa Monica, CA 90401
(213) 395-4667

*Hours:* 9:00 a.m.–6:00 p.m., Monday–Saturday
*Person to Contact:* Shawnee Issac-Smith, Director
*Founder/Owner:* Shawnee Issac-Smith (June 1987)
*Purpose:* To provide a comprehensive, yet sensitive delivery of (alternative) holistic health care.
*Facilities:* Two-story complete and fully staffed holistic health care facility. Movement room, group room for workshops, and flotation tank.
*Services:* Acupuncture, biofeedback, chiropractic, family practice, homeopathy, movement therapy, physical therapy, Rolfing, psychotherapy, flotation tank, sports medicine, massage, yoga, craniosacral therapy, and workshops offered on an ongoing basis.
*Visions and Goals:* The center's vision is to provide a nurturing and thorough environment with its focus on healing the "whole person."

# Center for Total Health

312 South Cedros, Solana Beach, CA 92075
(619) 755-6681

*Hours:* 9:00 a.m.–5:30 p.m., Monday–Friday
*Person to Contact:* Nancy Walls
*Founder/Owner:* Dr. Jason Doty (1976)
*Purpose:* To provide a comprehensive total health center that considers multidisciplinary approaches.
*Facilities:* Exercise center, health professionals, bookstore, and a color/sound research center, all in a 25,000-square-foot facility.
*Services:* Medical, chiropractic and psychological care. Physical therapy, nutrition and many others. Classes and seminars.
*Visions and Goals:* To provide a comprehensive array of service for all dimensions of life-style medicine.
*Miscellaneous:* The center is considered one of the most comprehensive facilities of its kind.

# Institute of Energetic Medicine

201 Lomas Santa Fe, Suite 201, Solana Beach, CA 92025
(619) 481-3314

*Hours:* 9:00 a.m.–6:00 p.m., Monday–Friday
*Person to Contact:* Candace McGinnis, Owner
*Founder/Owner:* Candace McGinnis and Bryan Stern (February 1986)
*Purpose:* To provide a complete wholistic healing environment that supports the total growth of each unique individual. We are a large center with eight practitioners and doctors working as a team in preventative and acute/chronic family care.
*Facilities:* Modern 3000-square-foot building one block from the ocean. Near motels and clean vegetarian restaurants.
*Services:* Acupuncture, chiropractic, colonics, homeopathy, herbs, physiotherapy, massage therapy, kirlian, psychology, and an M.D.
*Visions and Goals:* We are committed to education and research and to making a positive difference in how people perceive their health, life, and environment.

# Center for Attitudinal Healing

19 Main Street, Tiburon, CA 94920
(415) 435-5022

*Hours:* 9:00 a.m.–5:00 p.m., Monday–Friday
*Person to Contact:* Phoebe Lauren, Executive Director
*Founder:* Gerald G. Jampolsky, M.D. (1975)
*Owner:* Nonprofit organization
*Purpose:* The center was established to supplement traditional health care by providing an environment in which both children and adults faced with a life-threatening illness can actively participate in the process of attitudinal healing. The concept of attitudinal healing is based on the belief that it is possible to choose peace rather than conflict and love rather than fear. We believe that love is the most important healing force in the world. Attitudinal healing is the process of letting go of painful, fearful attitudes. When we release fear, only love remains. At the center, our definition of health is inner peace, and healing is the process of letting go of fear.
*Facilities:* The center is located on the waterfront in Tiburon, a 20-minute drive across the Golden Gate Bridge from San Francisco. Support groups meet at the center throughout the week. Center bookstore and gift store.
*Services:* Adult programs: life-threatened, AIDS/ARC/worried well, women with breast cancer, chronic illness, elders group, wellness group, support persons group. Young adults: life-threatened or catastrophic event. Children: children with life-threatening illness, their siblings and parents: children of parent with life-threatening illness. Also bereavement and loss and grief programs. AIDS Hot-Line for kids. Educational programs: volunteer program, Attitudinal Healing Training Conference, presentations, workshops, consultations, contracted services, and open house/orientation.
*Visions and Goals:* All who come to the center, including the staff and many volunteers, are there to find peace of mind by establishing a nonjudgmental, loving attitude toward themselves and others. We are committed to helping one another achieve the shift in perception from fear to love that facilitates the process of attitudinal healing. Our emphasis is on extending love and being of service to others. Everyone is recognized as a teacher; therefore, we are all students and teachers to each other as we learn the process of attitudinal healing.
*Materials Available:* Books and tapes by Dr. Jampolsky and others are sold at the center and by mail.

# Orr Hot Springs

13201 Orr Springs Road, Ukiah, CA 95482
(707) 462-6277

*Hours:* 10:00 a.m.–10:00 p.m., Friday–Sunday; 10:00 a.m.–6:00 p.m.,
  Monday
*Person to Contact:* Mr. Leslie Williams, Manager
*Founder:* Orr Family (1858)
*Owner:* Private corporation
*Purpose:* Caretakers of natural hot springs—providing an opportunity
  for the public to "take the waters." Operating a resort/retreat for city-
  dwellers seeking health and relaxation.
*Facilities:* Private cabins, camping group meeting/sleeping rooms,
  guest kitchen, dining room, communal hot tub, private bathtubs,
  communal soaking pool, swimming pool, and sauna.
*Services:* Massage.
*Visions and Goals:* To continue caretaking the hot springs while continuing to improve our facilities, gardens, services and atmosphere
  for the enjoyment of Orr Springs' visitors, employees, and owners.
*Materials Available:* Massage tables, slide projector, and screen.

# Round Mountain Cooperative Healing Center

1201 Parducci Road, Ukiah, CA 95482
(707) 462-3547

*Hours:* By arrangement
*Person to Contact:* Darca Nicholson, Director
*Founder/Owner:* Darca Nicholson (January 1978)
*Purpose:* Rest, recovery, and repair.
*Facilities:* Healing Center building, the Old Ranch House, pool,
  creeks, 160 acres to hike, access to 800 acres plus a 22-acre lake, out-
  buildings, and detached buildings.
*Services:* Colon Camp, special diets, exercise program, rest, medita-
  tion, classes in massage, and so forth.
*Visions and Goals:* Unity and love.

# Vichy Springs Resort
2605 Vichy Springs Road, Ukiah, CA 95482
(707) 462-9515

*Hours:* Sunrise–Sunset
*Person to Contact:* Gilbert Ashoff, President
*Founder:* William Day (1854)
*Owner:* Gilbert Ashoff
*Purpose:* Healing resort utilizing the naturally carbonated mineral-laden 90 degree waters.
*Facilities:* In spring 1989, overnight accommodations, RV parking, mineral baths, mineral plunge ( pool ), hiking on 680-acre ranch, restaurant.
*Services:* Massage therapy, hydrotherapy, medical clinic, and counseling. Also massage certification.
*Visions and Goals:* Addition of classes and workshops related to natural healing powers and wellness.
*Miscellaneous:* The mineral baths are available now; the balance of the resort is being renovated.

# Wellness Counseling Center and Holistic School of Massage
173 Seminary Avenue, Box 1199, Ukiah, CA 95482-0609
(707) 462-0609

*Hours:* 10:00 a.m.–5:00 p.m., Monday–Friday
*Person to Contact:* Virginia Romero, Director
*Founder/Owner:* Virginia Romero
*Purpose:* As an association of holistic health care professionals, we facilitate self-help life-styles on the three levels—body, mind and spirit. We offer ongoing programs and training for personal integration, counseling, life-style, and touch therapies.
*Facilities:* Classrooms and practitioners' treatment rooms available with a bookstore and herbstore.
*Services:* Center: Over 20 different services to choose from, including therapeutic massage, allergy/nutritional counseling, emotional clearing, and edu-kinesthetics. School of Massage: Classes in three career programs—Massage Practitioner, Natural Health Counselor, and Holistic Health Educator.
*Materials Available:* Books on herbs and natural health care, Nature's Sunshine herbal products, health products, and tapes.

## Astara, Inc.

800 W. Arrow Highway, P.O. Box 5003, Upland, CA 91785
(714) 981-4941 or 981-8033

*Hours:* 8:30 a.m.–4:45 p.m., Monday–Friday
*Person to Contact:* Pam Rau, Facilities Coordinator
*Founder/Owner:* Drs. Earlyne and Robert Chaney (1951)
*Purpose:* To provide information and experiences leading to self-realization through the study and practices of metaphysical principles.
*Facilities:* Ten-acre campus, including meditation gardens, chapel, classrooms, bookstore, cafeteria, and administrative/publishing offices. Facilities are available for use by nonprofit organizations. Overnight accommodations for 100 people, and dining facilities that will accommodate vegetarians.
*Services:* Classes, seminars, workshops, publications, crystal healing research clinic, counseling, prayer requests, peace meditation group, Sunday morning nondenominational New Age church service at 11:00 a.m.
*Materials Available:* Twenty-two books; 150 esoteric correspondence degree lessons, home study courses, including New Age Healing Methods; bardo tapes, and meditation posters.

## Avery Ranch

Box 155, Vallecito, CA 95251
(209) 533-2851

*Hours:* 9:30 a.m.–4:30 p.m.
*Person to Contact:* Jim Stearns, President
*Founder/Owner:* Jim Stearns
*Purpose:* Spiritual renewal, nature contact.
*Facilities:* Sauna, medicine wheel, sweathouse, rooms for 40 (double occupancy), dining lodge, basketball, volleyball, hiking, and a river nearby.
*Services:* Complete dining facilities, all styles from vegetarian to French.
*Visions and Goals:* To provide a facility and service to promote spiritual renewal for humanity and the planet.

# Mount Madonna Center

445 Summit Road, Watsonville, CA 95076
(408) 722-7175

*Hours:* 9:00 a.m.–5:00 p.m., Monday–Wednesday; 11:00 a.m.–5:00
p.m., Thursday–Saturday
*Person to Contact:* Dr. Brajesh Friedberg, Program Director
*Founder/Owner:* Hanuman Fellowship (1978)
*Purpose:* To nurture the creative arts and the health sciences within a
context of spiritual growth.
*Facilities:* Dormitory rooms for 4 to 7; semiprivate rooms for 2 to 3;
private rooms. Campgrounds located in redwood groves include running water, center tents, and sites for personal tents. Recreational
facilities, hiking trails, volleyball and basketball courts, a small lake,
and a library. Bookstore, gift store and Ayurvedic herb store.
*Services:* Health and healing, yoga, fine arts, personal and spiritual
growth. Accommodations for private rental groups from 12 to 300.
Oil massage and herbal steam baths, personal retreat space,
work/study arrangements and ongoing weekly classes in yoga and
scriptural study.
*Materials Available:* Large selection of metaphysical books and tapes
as well as clothing, gift items, and daily necessities.

# Wilbur Hot Springs Health Sanctuary

Star Route, Williams, CA 95987
(916) 473-2306

*Hours:* 9:00 a.m.–9:00 p.m., 7 days a week
*Person to Contact:* Nancy Woodworth, Manager
*Founded:* 1865. "New Age" in 1972.
*Owner:* Dr. Richard Louis Miller
*Purpose:* Healing and health. A personal and/or group retreat.
*Facilities:* Hot springs, private rooms, meeting rooms and a commer-
cial kitchen. Extreme privacy in a 24-acre private valley. We also
have a resident artist program and extended stays for health
purposes.
*Services:* Massage and occasional seminars.
*Visions and Goals:* Health, peace, and graceful living.
*Materials Available:* Brochures.

# More Centers/Retreats

*Heartsong Center*   1412 Solano Avenue, Albany, CA 94706
(415-527-4823)
*Rockridge Health*   828 San Pablo Avenue, Albany, CA 94705
*Center for Creative Change*   2065 Arnold Way, Alpine, CA 92001
(619-445-8877)
*Psynetics Foundation*   1212 East Lincoln Avenue, Anaheim, CA
92805 (714-533-2311)
*Auroville Association*   212 Farley Drive, Aptos, CA 95003
*Stevea Retreat Center*   Box 1155, Arcata, CA 95521 (707-433-8365)
*Berkeley Psychic Institute*   2436 Haste Street, Berkeley, CA 94704
(415-548-8020)
*Berkeley Women's Health Collective*   2908 Ellsworth, Berkeley, CA
94705 (415-843-6194)
*Friends of EKR*   2909 Regent Street, #3, Berkeley, CA 94705
(415-549-1561)
*Melia Foundation*   1525 Shattuck Avenue, Suite G, Berkeley, CA
94709 (415-845-6966)
*School of Lost Borders*   Box 55, Big Pine, CA 93513
*Hill of the Hawk*   Box 48, Big Sur, CA 93920 (408-667-2508)
*Ventana Inn*   Big Sur, CA 93920 (408-628-6500)
*Commonweal*   Box 316, Bolinas, CA 94924 (415-868-0970)
*Gerson Institute*   P.O. Box 430, Bonita, CA 92002 (714-267-1150)
*Los Angeles Center for Living*   1600 N. Sierra, Bonita, CA 90046
(213-850-0877)
*Natural Environment Health Center*   P.O. Box 11, Brookdale, CA
95007 (408-338-2363)
*The Ashram Healthort*   Box 8009, Calabasas, CA 91302
(818-888-0232)
*Hideaway Hot Springs Resort*   1412 Fairway, Calistoga, CA 94515
(707-942-4108)
*Charan Springs Farm*   Route 1, Box 521, Cambria, CA 93428
(805-927-8289)
*Nos Amis/Our Friends*   7519 Sausalito Avenue, Canoga Park, CA
91307 (818-346-1465)
*The Self-Center*   7108 Remmet Avenue, Canoga Park, CA 91303
(818-704-8464)
*Institute for Creative Health*   1501 Summit Avenue, Cardiff, CA
92007 (619-942-5869)
*John-David Learning Institute*   2441 Impala Drive, Carlsbad, CA
92008 (619-931-0456)

*Window of the West*   Star Route, Box 94, Carmel Valley, CA 93924
(408-659-0433)

*Clearlake Medical Center*   Box 3370, Clearlake, CA 95422
(707-994-9486)

*Round Valley Indian Health Center*   P.O. Box 247, Covelo, CA 95428
(707-983-2981)

*El Reposo Spa*   66334 W. 5th Street, Desert Hot Springs, CA 92240
(619-329-6632)

*Moors Health Spa*   12673 Reposo Way, Desert Hot Springs, CA 92240

*Sam's Family Spa*   70875 Dillon Road, Desert Hot Springs, CA 92240
(619-329-6457)

*Vita-Dell Spa*   13495 Palm Drive, Desert Hot Springs, CA 92240
(714-329-6200)

*The Crystal Rainbow*   P.O. Box 912, El Cajon, CA 92002
(619-440-5973)

*Kairos*   298 Sunset Drive, Encinitas, CA 92024 (619-942-2191)

*Pathways Life Enrichment Center*   681 Encinitas Boulevard, Encinitas, CA 92024 (619-436-9360)

*Holy Spirit Retreat Center*   4316 Lanai Road, Encino, CA 91436
(818-784-4515)

*Vital Health Center*   17200 Ventura Blvd., Suite 305, Encino, CA
91316 (213-986-0886)

*Actualism Wholistic Center*   739 E. Pennsylvania, #D, Escondido,
CA 92026 (714-741-7827)

*Dances of Universal Peace*   114 Forrest Avenue, Fairfax, CA 94930
(415-453-8159)

*High Point Foundation*   5337 North Millbrook, Fresno, CA 93710
(209-222-5695)

*The Center Gallery*   7052 Orangewood Avenue, Suite 8, Garden
Grove, CA 92641

*Healing Light Center*   138 N. Maryland, Glendale, CA 91206
(213-244-8607)

*Well-Being Community Center*   Box 549, Graton, CA 95472
(707-823-9355)

*Pacific School of Healing Arts*   44000 Fish Rock Road, Gualala, CA
95445 (707-884-3138)

*Wildwood Resort-Retreat*   Box 78, Guerneville, CA 95446
(707-632-5321)

*The Inner Vision Center*   3774 5th Avenue, Hillcrest, CA 92103
(619-692-0238)

*Julian Preventive Medicine Clinic*   1654 Cahuenga, Hollywood, CA
90028 (213-466-0126)

*Thunder Institute*   Box 160, Horse Creek, CA 96045 (916-496-3266)

*Center for Conscious Living*   2223 Main Street, #41, Huntington
Beach, CA 92648 (714-969-4202)

*Goldenwind Dreamers Lodge*    19732 Potomac Lane, Huntington Beach, CA 92646 (714-962-2926)
*Inner Visions*    2223 Main Street, #47-B, Huntington Beach, CA 92648 (714-960-9995)
*Terra Nova Institute*    Coast Highway 1, Box 69, Jenner, CA 95450 (707-865-2377)
*Brockway Springs Resort*    Box 276, King's Beach, CA 95719 (916-546-4201)
*Edenic Light Center*    25258 Cabot Road, #263, Laguna Hills, CA 92653 (714-675-4722)
*Health Institute of San Diego*    6970 Central Avenue, Lemon Grove, CA 92045 (619-464-3346)
*Hidden Valley Sanctuary*    Lone Pine, CA 93545
*Three Mountain Foundation*    Box 1180, Lone Pine, CA 93545 (619-876-4702)
*Tzaddi Center*    321 Ximeno Avenue, Long Beach, CA 90814 (213-438-9706)
*Friends of EKR*    1917 Baxter Street, Los Angeles, CA 90039 (213-661-9464)
*Learning for Health*    1314 Westwood Boulevard,#107, Los Angeles, CA 90024 (213-474-6929)
*Life Production*    249 S. Manhattan Place, #C, Los Angeles, CA 90004 (213-382-0316)
*Play Mountain Place*    6063 Hargis Street, Los Angeles, CA 90034 (213-870-4381)
*Self-Realization Fellowship*    3880 San Rafael Avenue, Los Angeles, CA 90065 (213-225-2471)
*Shaw Health Center*    5336 Fontain Avenue, Los Angeles, CA 90029 (213-467-5200)
*Shirley MacLaine's Center*    c/o P.O. Box 67F00, Los Angeles, CA 90067
*Thomas Institute of Metaphysics*    4100½ W. Pico Boulevard, Los Angeles, CA 90019 (213-733-2633)
*World Synergy Institute*    P.O. Box 24242, Los Angeles, CA 90024 (213-821-1302)
*Mercy Hot Springs*    Box 1363, Los Banos, CA 93635
*The Mendocino Institute*    Box 1928, Mendocino, CA 95460 (707-937-2622)
*Holistic Healing Center*    1050 Chestnut Street, #202, Menlo Park, CA 94025 (415-321-8020)
*Spiritual Emergence Network*    250 Oak Grove Avenue, Menlo Park, CA 94025 (415-327-2776)
*Vallombrosa Center*    250 Oak Grove Avenue, Menlo Park, CA 94025 (415-325-5614)
*Trager Institute*    10 Old Mill Street, Mill Valley, CA 94941 (415-388-2688)

*Mono Hot Springs*   Mono Hot Springs, CA 93642

*Willow Women's Center*   6517 Dry Creek Road, Napa, CA 94558
(707-944-8173)

*Aquarian Institute*   2939 Galindo Street, Oakland, CA 94601
(415-534-1856)

*Dolphin Holistic Center*   3641 Diamond, Oakland, CA 94611
(415-531-5509)

*East Bay Center for Attitudinal Healing*   3534 Lakeshore, Oakland,
CA 94609 (415-893-5683)

*SYDA Foundation & Meditation Center*   1107 Stanford Avenue, Oakland, CA 94611 (415-655-8677)

*Avanta Network*   139 Forest Avenue, Palo Alto, CA 94301
(415-327-1424)

*Wellspring Renewal Center*   Box 332, Philo, CA 95446
(707-895-3893)

*Village Oz*   P.O. Box 147, Point Arena, CA 95468 (707-882-2449)

*Medical Self-Care*   P.O. Box 1000, Pt. Reyes, CA 94956
(415-663-8462)

*Healing & Spiritual Center*   Box 3162, Rancho Santa Fe, CA 92067
(619-756-0641)

*Transformational Arts Institute*   1380 Pacific Street, Redlands, CA
92373 (714-793-0054)

*The Corona Light*   12702 Magnolia, #8, Riverside, CA 91720
(714-736-1172)

*Womankind Health Clinic*   2720 Capital Avenue, Suite 105,
Sacramento, CA 95816 (916-448-5463)

*Center of Light*   Box 22367, San Diego, CA 92122 (619-560-4248)

*Friends of EKR*   1046 Leroy Street, San Diego, CA 92106
(619-222-0104)

*Life Purpose Institute*   7801 Mission Center Court, #228, San Diego,
CA 92108 (619-296-5800)

*Pacific Institute for Healing Arts*   7242 Clairemont Mesa Boulevard,
San Diego, CA 92111 (619-565-8777)

*Preventative Health Center*   3330 3rd Avenue, #400, San Diego, CA
92103 (619-291-0261)

*The Pacific Ability Center*   5525 Sandburg Avenue, San Diego, CA
92122 (619-458-0505)

*Buena Vista Women's Center*   2000 Van Ness Avenue, San Francisco,
CA 94104 (415-771-5000)

*Center for Applied Intuition*   2046 Clement Street, San Francisco,
CA 94121 (415-221-1280)

*Center for Self Healing*   1714-1718 Taraval Street, San Francisco, CA
94116 (415-665-9574)

*Center for Release & Integration*   1057 Steiner Street, San Francisco,
CA 94115 (415-929-0119)

*Fort Help Counseling Center*   169 11th Street, San Francisco, CA
94103 (415-864-4357)
*Friends of EKR*   41 Carl Street, #C, San Francisco, CA 94117
(415-564-1750)
*Friends of EKR*   3726 16th Street, San Francisco, CA 94114
(415-861-2857)
*Holistic Health Center*   2872 Folsom Street, San Francisco, CA
94110 (415-285-2909)
*Quadrinity Center*   2295 Palou Avenue, San Francisco, CA 94124
(415-397-0466)
*The Color Research Institute*   2727 Polk Street, #2, San Francisco,
CA 94109 (415-474-6375)
*Yoga Society of San Francisco*   2872 Folsom Street, San Francisco,
CA 94110 (415-285-5537)
*Aesclepian Healing Center*   1752 Lincoln Avenue, San Rafael, CA
94901 (415-453-1813)
*Dovetail Institute*   160 Bret Harte Road, San Rafael, CA 94901
(415-461-9521)
*Radiant Life Center*   824 5th Street, San Rafael, CA 94901
(415-459-6798)
*Center for Esoteric Studies*   533 E. Anapanu Street, Santa Barbara,
CA 93103
*Human Relations Center*   5200 Hollister Avenue, Santa Barbara, CA
93111 (805-967-4557)
*Spiritual Science Institute*   330 East Canon Perdido, #B, Santa Bar-
bara, CA 93101
*Center for Attitudinal Healing*   2803 Branaforte Drive, Santa Cruz,
CA 95065 (408-458-3675)
*Friends of EKR*   336 8th Avenue, Santa Cruz, CA 95062
(408-462-0585)
*Holistic Health Care*   1703 Wilshire Boulevard, Santa Monica, CA
90403 (213-453-4565)
*Wholistic Medical/Counseling Center*   1703 Wilshire Boulevard,
Santa Monica, CA 90403 (213-451-9997)
*Friends of EKR*   P.O. Box 6231, Santa Rosa, CA 95406 (707-528-7046)
*Hippocrates*   475 Gate Five Road, #100, Sausalito, CA 94965
(415-332-5866)
*Campbell Hot Springs*   Box 234, Sierraville, CA 96126
(916-994-8984)
*Vision Quest*   3200 E. Los Angeles Avenue, Simi Valley, CA 93063
(805-527-7297)
*Holistic Healing Arts Clinic*   312 S. Cedros, Solana Beach, CA 92075
(619-755-6681)

*Joshua Institute of Light*   871 Stevens Avenue, #1317, Solana Beach, CA 92075 (619-755-7574)

*World Healing Center*   725 Seabright Lane, Solana Beach, CA 92075

*Paraiso Hot Springs*   Soledad, CA 93960 (408-678-2882)

*Monterey Bay Center for Attitudinal Healing*   P.O. Box 1147, Soquel, CA 95073 (408-429-8142)

*Ella's Hide-A-Way Hot Springs*   Box 101, Tecopa, CA 92389

*Tecopa Hot Springs Resort*   Box 327, Tecopa, CA 92389 (619-852-4373)

*Akashic Center & Bookstore*   1414 Thousand Oaks Boulevard, Thousand Oaks, CA 91362 (805-495-5824)

*Foundation for Inner Peace*   Box 635, Tiburon, CA 94920

*Sundoor*   P.O. Box 669, Twain Harte, CA 95383 (209-928-3906)

*Healing Arts Center*   17280 Saticoy Street, Van Nuys, CA 91406 (818-343-0339)

*Shastasong*   16742 Middlecoff Court, Lake Shastina, Weed, CA 96094 (916-938-3659)

*Stewart Mineral Springs*   Route 1, Box 1093, Weed, CA 96094 (916-938-2222)

*The Ryoho Center*   1539 Sawtelle, #12, West Los Angeles, CA 90025 (213-477-0909)

*Emandel—A Farm on a River*   16501 Hearst Road, Willits, CA 95490 (707-459-5439)

# Part IV: The Southwest

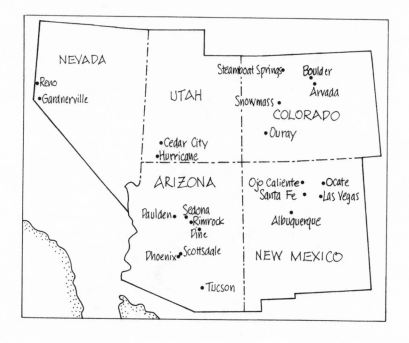

# Feather Mountain Conference Center

P.O. Box 670, Paulden, AZ 86334
(602) 445-0911

*Hours:* 9:00 a.m.–5:00 p.m., Monday–Friday
*Founder/Owner:* Brugh Joy and Duane and Phyllis Groce
*Purpose:* A center available to rent to groups for retreats and seminars. Individual retreat space is available also.
*Facilities:* Privacy and solitude. Large spa. Meals included. State-of-the-art audiovisual equipment in meeting room.
*Services:* Conferences, seminars, and workshops such as Four-Day Spiritual/Meditation Retreat, Foundational Conferences, Initiations into Intuitive and Third Eye States, Woman Workshop, and Dream-time Seminar.
*Miscellaneous:* Brugh Joy moved from his old site of Lucerne Valley to the Feather Mountain Conference Center in September 1988. A teaching, healing, renewing conference center is under way, with a great seminar room, dining facility, large outdoor spa, and acccommodations already under construction. It will also serve as a conference facility for other seminar leaders which will accommodate up to 40 people. Personal retreat space will also be available.

# Arizona Metaphysical Society

3336 N. 32nd Street, Suite 101, Phoenix, AZ 85018
(602) 956-1676

*Hours:* 9:00 a.m.–5:00 p.m, Monday–Friday
*Person to Contact:* Dr. Frank Alder, Director
*Founder/Owner:* Dr. Frank Alder (1974)
*Purpose:* To serve as a vehicle for people to achieve the balance between the spiritual and physical expressions in their lives.
*Facilities:* On-site product display room and lecture room.
*Services:* Lectures and two-day workshops presented internationally; six-day seminar, "Carousel of Growth," designed to help individuals understand a self-transformation and spiritual evolution, which is attended by people from all over the world; counseling and healing.
*Visions and Goals:* Plans are now under way for construction of a worldwide facility to serve as a hub for all aspects of spiritual expression and research.
*Materials Available:* Books, audiotapes and videotapes authorized by Dr. Alder; crystals and healing essences.

# The A.R.E. Clinic
4017 N. 40th Street, Phoenix, AZ 85018
(602) 955-7729

*Hours:* 8:30 a.m.–5:00 p.m., Monday–Friday
*Person to Contact:* Venessa Hoyt, Director of Intake
*Founder/Owner:* William McGarvey, M.D., and Gladys McGarvey,
  M.D. (1970)
*Purpose:* Healing whole person, body, mind, and spirit.
*Facilities:* Two buildings plus residence.
*Services:* Medical and laboratory services. Various therapies, including
  energy medicine-ETA, acuscope, biofeedback, counseling; massage
  therapy-lymphatic, massage, and colonics. Also patterning therapy
  for neurological dysfunctions, and educational services.
*Visions and Goals:* At this time we are only one center. We would like
  to expand into other states and additional ventures.
*Materials Available:* Cayce Corner, our retail store, carries books, vitamins, herbs and Cayce remedies.


# Healing Pines
P.O. Box 658, Pine, AZ 85544
(602) 476-3392

*Hours:* 12:00 noon – 8:00 p.m.
*Person to Contact:* Manager on duty
*Founder:* Stan Kalson (1984)
*Owner:* Partnership
*Purpose:* To provide rest and quiet in a secluded forest setting and an
  opportunity to relax in the clean mountain air and unwind from city
  stress. Our name was chosen to identify the healing qualities of
  fresh air, clean water, green trees, and quiet environments.
*Facilities:* Comfortable cottages fully furnished with two bedrooms,
  one bath, fireplace, living/dining area, kitchen, and covered front
  porch.
*Services:* A restful place. Massage therapy available in the privacy of
  your own cottage. Area recreation includes boating, horseback riding, hiking, quaint restaurants, and cross country skiing.
*Visions and Goals:* To expand our operation so more people can come
  to witness the peace and quiet of Healing Pines and realize the
  importance of reconnecting themselves to the healing qualities of
  nature.

# Golden Phoenix Healing and Light Center

P.O. Box 969, Rimrock, AZ 86335
(602) 567-4937

*Hours:* 8:00 a.m.–10:00 p.m., 7 days a week
*Person to Contact:* Jane Greven
*Founder/Owner:* Rev. Mona Fore (1986)
*Purpose:* To make available to the general public alternative healing programs that enable people to heal and cure themselves of disease naturally. To offer a "whole person" program that addresses the physical, emotional, mental, and spiritual levels simultaneously.
*Facilities:* Peaceful 14-acre hilltop residential retreat near Sedona, Arizona; shared and private guest rooms, sinfully delicious natural food; conference and therapy rooms.
*Services:* Systemic (full-body) detoxification, specific organ(s) detoxification, customized detoxification, and rebuilding programs that address specific diseases. Other natural therapies offered include nutritional and health counseling including supplements, herbology, mineral baths, massage, acupressure, shiatsu, color and sound therapy, crystal healing, movement therapy, visualization and meditation. Other services offered include channeled readings, astrological counseling, transformational seminars, vision quests, and sweat lodge.
*Visions and Goals:* A center that offers a multitude of alternative healing methods to restore physical health and inspire "Aliveness," from simple rejuvenation to treatment of serious and terminal diseases.
*Materials Available:* Books: *Personal Karmic Astrology Workbook* and *Karmic Astrology of Relationship* by Mona Fore, Director. Crystal healing patterns with specifically taped music. Herb mixtures and teas. Crystals, gems, minerals, and art objects.

# New Age Educational Center

10405 N. Scottsdale Road, Suite 2, Scottsdale, AZ 85253
(602) 483-3737

*Hours:* 9:00 a.m.–5:00 p.m., Monday–Friday
*Person to Contact:* Gayle Stauffer, Owner
*Founder/Owner:* Gayle Stauffer (May 1980)
*Purpose:* To create and maintain an educational research and networking center enabling those of like mind to have a common ground to meet and exchange information.
*Facilities:* Private counseling offices and classroom.
*Services:* Group and individual counseling; ongoing classes in all areas including healing, Reiki, regression therapy, UFO research, PSI phenomena, meditation, visualization, and channeling. In addition, we do weekend seminars with guest leaders.
*Visions and Goals:* To always keep the doors open to new ideas and bridge the gaps where they may exist. Open a bookstore within a year.
*Materials Available:* Books and tapes.


# The Rim Institute

November-April: 6835 Pepper Tree Lane, Scottsdale, AZ 85253
(602) 941-7121
May-October: HCR Box 162D, Payson, AZ 85541
(602) 478-4727

*Hours:* 9:00 a.m.–5:00 p.m., Monday–Friday
*Founder:* Robert D. Mosby, Ph.D., and Joan B. Norris, M.C. (1983)
Owner: Nonprofit
*Purpose:* To help facilitate the process of each individual coming to know the totality of his or her being. To provide a physical setting where personal exploration can take place in an atmosphere of a community of seekers, each exploring his or her own unique path.
*Facilities:* Main cabin with check-in office, dining area, yurts, and a shop with special books and other treasures.
*Services:* Workshops and seminars as well as other programs including the Individual Retreat, the Work-Study Program, and Passages. The Rim Institute is also the regional coordinator for the Spiritual Emergence Network. Gourmet health cuisine and daily meditations. Massage, yoga, astrology, past-life therapy available by appointment.
*Materials Available:* Cassette tape, videotape and book library.

# The Healing Center of Arizona

25 Wilson Canyon Road, Sedona, AZ 86336
(602) 282-7710

*Hours:* 9:00 a.m.–9:00 p.m., Monday–Friday
*Person to Contact:* John Paul Weber, Director, or Kate Weber, Executive
  Director
*Founder/Owner:* John Paul and Kate Weber (1981)
*Purpose:* Individual and group services aimed at integrating body/
  mind/spirit to restore and enhance one's natural healing potential.
*Facilities:* Three comfortable guest rooms, steam/sauna/spa dome,
  large meditation dome, large conference dome, medicine wheel and
  sweat lodge, waterfalls, gardens and decks, hiking and swimming.
*Services:* Individual and group therapeutic retreats, classes and conferences and broad range of therapies; space available for workshops;
  weekly World Peace Meditation; bed and breakfast accommodations.

# Synergy Center

4541 E. Fort Lowell Road, Suite 211, Tucson, AZ 85712
(602) 881-7171

A working cooperative building housing four organizations: Institute for Cosmic Awareness, Harmony and Health Foundation, Natural Balance Wholistic Health, and Cloud Nine Flotation.

*Visions and Goals:* To complete a new 44,000-square-foot facility in the next three years, and to offer a complete urban center for wellness.

## Institute for Cosmic Awareness

*Hours:* 10:00 a.m.–6:00 p.m., Monday–Friday
*Person to Contact:* Dorothy Summers or Marcia Wetstein
*Founder:* Dorothy Summers and Marcia Wetstein (April 1988)
*Owner:* Nonprofit
*Purpose:* A community-based spiritual center established to explore spiritual healing and unfoldment through the metaphysical arts.
*Services:* Weekly classes in psychic arts, tarot, and past-life readings, an open class on spiritual and psychic unfoldment called Pathways to Power, and individual sessions in past-life and akashic readings, spiritual healing, psychometry, and channeling. Also sponsor many psychic fairs.
*Miscellaneous:* Both Dorothy Summers and Marcia Wetstein are ordained ministers.

## Harmony and Health Foundation

*Hours:* 10:00 a.m.–7:00 p.m., 7 days a week, by appointment only
*Person to Contact:* David Kaler, Director
*Founder:* David Kaler (April 1984)
*Owner:* Nonprofit
*Purpose:* Community-based organization established to assist in exploring physical, emotional, mental, and spiritual self-help approaches to health and healing which are harmonious with the laws of nature.
*Services:* We offer a variety of ongoing daily classes in yoga, meditation, and spiritual development, and special workshops during the month designed to open the individual to all aspects of health and

healing. Through our practitioner cooperative we also offer private consultations and services by highly trained, certified, and licensed therapists in a wide variety of practices including regression therapy, graphoanalysis, neuromuscular balancing, rebirthing, energy and chakra balancing, shiatsu, therapeutic massage, polarity, acupressure, mind and body integration, reflexology, hypnotherapy, psychic-reflex-palmistry, clairvoyance, channeling, photograph reading, nutrition, and therapeutic touch.

## Natural Balance Wholistic Health

*Hours:* 9:00 a.m.–7:00 p.m., Monday–Friday; 10:00 a.m –5:00 p.m., Saturday

*Person to Contact:* Marc Haberman, Director

*Founder/Owner:* Marc Haberman (March 1981)

*Purpose:* To provide comprehensive wellness programs for individuals, businesses, and other organizations. We provide a basis of wellness from which the individual can understand him/herself better, improve relationships, and create a more satisfying work environment and improved quality of life.

*Services:* Workshops are offered in vision improvement, humor, and massage. In addition, individual private sessions in polarity, therapeutic massage, shiatsu, acupressure, Kofutu balancing, nutritional counseling, aromatherapy, cranial-sacral work, joint release, Swedish therapeutic massage, psychic and tarot readings.

*Visions and Goals:* We believe that to be happy and healthy one must take an active role in one's growth process.

## Cloud Nine Flotation

*Hours:* 10:00 a.m.–10:00 p.m., Monday–Friday; 11:00 a.m.–3:00 p.m., Saturday and Sunday

*Person to Contact:* Kalyn Wolf

*Founder/Owner:* Kalyn Wolf (May 1986)

*Purpose:* To lead people in stress reduction, relaxation, and self-development using gentle and noninvasive techniques.

*Facilities:* Flotation tank, which is a little larger than a twin-size bed, filled with 10 to 12 inches of water, to which great quantities of epsom salts are added.

*Services:* Long-lasting stress relief, relief from discomfort or pain, and time out to explore one's inner self. Floating creates a deep state of relaxation that in just 60 minutes can allow you to feel great for a week. As a floater, you will experience what it is like to lie on your back and feel as weightless as an astronaut in space.

# Canyon Ranch Spa

8600 E. Rockcliff Road, Tucson, AZ 85715
(602) 749-9000

*Hours:* 7:00 a.m.–5:00 p.m.
*Person to Contact:* Reservations
*Founder/Owner:* Enid and Mel Zuckerman (1979)
*Purpose:* Programs in fitness, nutrition, health, sports, and stress
    reduction. Tools to revive and energize the body, mind, and spirit.
*Facilities:* Seventy acres, complete spa, 8 tennis courts, racquet-
    ball/squash courts, 9 gyms, weight rooms, beauty salon, medical
    complex, golf nearby. Recently opened the Life Enhancement Cen-
    ter offering a "spa within a spa" designed for more intimate groups of
    up to 40 persons.
*Services:* Fitness consultations and classes, massage therapists, skin
    care specialists, herbalists, wellness counselors, certified fitness
    instructors, sports pros, psychologists, registered dietitians, exercise
    physiologists, and nurses.
*Visions and Goals:* To educate, demonstrate, and provide a practical,
    personal strategy to life-style improvement and total wellness.
*Materials Available:* For brochures and other information, call
    1-800-742-9000; in Canada, call 1-800-327-9090.

# Energy-Consciousness

8425 Everett Way, #E, Arvada, CO 80005
(303) 425-8709

*Hours:* 9:00 a.m.–5:00 p.m., Monday–Friday
*Person to Contact:* Elizabeth Mylonas, Director
*Founder/Owner:* Alex and Elizabeth Mylonas (1980)
*Purpose:* To facilitate movement of energy and consciousness in
    people.
*Facilities:* One classroom/group room, two small session spaces and a
    mountain retreat for one-day workshops.
*Services:* Private sessions, three classes in energy-consciousness,
    energy healing sessions.
*Visions and Goals:* To free energy and consciousness to end separation
    that causes all dis-ease.
*Materials Available:* A book, *How to Find God and Have Fun Doing
    It*; the Pathwork Guide lectures.

## Emergence—Center for Transformational Arts

P.O. Box 1425, Boulder, CO 80305
(303) 449-3305

*Hours:* 9:00 a.m.–5:00 p.m., Monday–Friday
*Person to Contact:* Katie Marks, Director
*Founder/Owner:* Katie Marks, M.S.W.
*Purpose:* Offers programs to bring deeper realization of life purpose and soul path, catalyzing healing and transformation, connecting us with inner wisdom, power, and creativity.
*Services:* Ongoing classes, lectures, workshops, and training seminars as well as private healing, counseling, and channeling sessions. Subjects include sound and healing, polarity and intuitive healing, hearts of power and journeys of initiation, Woman, Wisdom, and Power, Sacred dance, song and ritual, emergence and empowerment.
*Visions and Goals:* To create a network of ceremonial studies and transformational therapists worldwide. To integrate many modalities of healing with creative and ritual arts. To share the power of ritual and ceremony.
*Materials Available:* Tapes, books, and audiotapes.

## Wiesbaden Hot Springs and Lodgings

P.O. Box 349, 625 5th Avenue, Ouray, CO 81427
(303) 325-4347

*Hours:* 8:00 a.m.–10:00 p.m., 7 days a week
*Person to Contact:* Mary Linda Wright-Minter, Owner
*Founder:* Originally built by the Buchanans in 1879
*Purpose:* Over the past 50 years, the Wiesbaden has evolved into a small, personable spa frequented by persons from around the world. Because of its therapeutic qualities, unique hot springs vapor cave, and other facilities, the Wiesbaden is recognized as unequaled for relaxation and rejuvenation.
*Facilities:* Natural hot springs, sauna with hot springs soaking pool, natural vapor cave with soaking pool, outdoor hot springs swimming pool, and enclosed private outdoor natural soaking pools. Exercise and dance room. Individually decorated rooms.
*Services:* Therapeutic acupressure massage, therapeutic Swedish massage, facials, and reflexology.
*Visions and Goals:* To be a place of healing and rejuvenation for persons from around the world.
*Materials Available:* Universal equipment and aerobic and exercise videos.

# Windstar Foundation

2317 Snowmass Creek Road, Snowmass, CO 81654
(303) 927-4777

*Hours:* 9:00 a.m.–5:00 p.m., Monday–Friday
*Founder:* John Denver and Thomas Crum (1976)
*Owner:* Nonprofit
*Purpose:* To create a context for people to take direct action for a peaceful, sustainable future. The Windstar Foundation expresses a profound belief in humanity's ability to live in harmony with one another and the earth.
*Facilities:* One thousand acres nestled in the Rocky Mountains near Aspen, Colorado.
*Services:* Workshops, apprenticeships, and internships are available in bioshelter design and food production, high-altitude gardening and landscaping, small-scale farming, and land stewardship. The annual Choices for the Future Symposium provides the opportunity to interact with worldwide leaders in such fields as education, global security, peaceful exploration of space, conservation, ecology, and effective service.
*Materials Available:* Quarterly magazine, *The Windstar Journal*, and information on the "Biodome."

# Rocky Mountain Wellness Spa and Institute

P.O. Box 777, Steamboat Springs, CO 80477
(303) 879-7772; in Canada (800) 345-7771 or (800) 345-7770

*Hours:* 9:00 a.m.–5:00 p.m., Monday–Friday
*Person to Contact:* Larry or Dorothy Allingham, Directors
*Founder/Owner:* Larry and Dorothy Allingham (1983)
*Purpose:* To pass on the ways in which the Allinghams revitalized their lives after burnout, losing a lifetime business, and poor health. A wholistic/ scientific approach to giving each individual the knowledge to deal with stress, nutrition, exercise, smoking, cholesterol, blood sugar, and beauty for a higher quality of life.
*Facilities:* Four-star lodging, exercise rooms, conference room, dining room, indoor/outdoor pool, jacuzzi, and sauna.
*Services:* Nutritional computer analysis, vitamin and mineral analysis, metabolism efficiency analysis, massage, body control program, weight loss/gain, and stop smoking programs.
*Visions and Goals:* To help people find love in themselves and love in the world. To help people deal with their fears, worries, and despairs of life.
*Materials Available:* Exercise equipment, library, and videotapes.

# Sierra Spirit Ranch

3000 Pinenut Road, Gardnerville, NV 89410
(702) 782-7011

*Hours:* 24 hours a day, 7 days a week
*Person to Contact:* Chris or Robin Irwin
*Founder/Owner:* Chris and Robin Irwin (October 1987)
*Purpose:* Peace and quiet and seclusion. We are surrounded by beautiful countryside with Pinenut Creek and three ponds, only 40 minutes from Lake Tahoe.
*Facilities:* Four rooms (3 bedrooms in modern ranch house and one separate studio guest house with kitchen), swimming pool, hot tub, horses, bicycles, volleyball, horseshoes, and hiking.
*Services:* Bed and breakfast; massage by appointment.
*Visions and Goals:* Expand into private cabins with more recreational activities offered.

# Joy Lake Mountain Seminar Center

P.O. Box 1328, Dept. T., Reno, NV 89504
(702) 323-0378

*Hours:* 8:00 a.m.–4:30 p.m., Monday–Saturday
*Person to Contact:* Alan Morvay, Director
*Founder/Owner:* Alan and Jacque Morvay (1983)
*Purpose:* To integrate the physical, mental, and spiritual aspects of personal growth and self-development.
*Facilities:* Located in the heart of the eastern Sierra, Joy Lake Mountain Seminar Center is located on 80 acres of land, which includes 4-acre Joy Lake, ponderosa pine tree forest, and overlooking Washoe Lake. A western village, bookstore, cabins and yurts, camping facilities, herbal garden, and medicine wheel.
*Services:* Weekend and five-day workshops in personal growth and self-development. A three-week masters program in crystal healing, classes approved for nursing and college credit, and workshops focusing on shamanism and women's spirituality. Gourmet vegetarian meals.
*Visions and Goals:* To provide a place for people to grow and develop through a seasonal workshop series.

# The Ayurvedic Wellness Center and Institute

11311 Menaul N.E., Suite A, Albuquerque, NM 87112
(505) 291-9698

*Hours:* 9:30 a.m.–4:30 p.m., Monday–Thursday
*Person to Contact:* Front desk
*Founder/Owner:* Dr. Vasant Lad (1981)
*Purpose:* To spread the science of self-healing, Ayurveda. Ayurveda, a sanskrit word for "the science of life," is a fundamental system which treats the body, mind, and consciousness. It has been practiced in India for at least 5,000 years.
*Facilities:* Classroom, clinic, and reading room.
*Services:* Eight-month in-depth program in the science of Ayurvedic medicine. Through the Ayurvedic Wellness Center, a variety of services are provided including individualized health education, lifestyle counseling, doshic diet, exercise, herbs, pancha and purva karma, and rasayana.
*Visions and Goals:* To give humanity the keys to their own selfhealing.
*Materials Available:* Books and herbs.

# Ocamora Foundation

Box 43, Ocate, NM 87734
(505) 666-2389

*Hours:* 9:00 a.m.–5:00 p.m., Monday–Friday
*Person to Contact:* Pattie Cavalletto, President
*Founder:* Pattie Cavalletto and Michael Broome (1981)
*Owner:* Nonprofit organization
*Purpose:* To provide support for personal solitary retreat and for certain meditative and creative group retreats. Simplicity–Solitude–Sanctuary: a return to essential vision.
*Facilities:* The remoteness and beauty of the Ocamora valley offers an expansive intimacy with nature. Private retreat rooms, tipis, and tents. Meditation and movement sanctuary.
*Services:* Year-round personal retreat. Enjoy the peace of true rest with a loving and supportive environment. Two meals and an evening snack will be served to you daily. Group retreats, like the Vipassana Meditation Retreat with Bhante Gunaratana which is silent and limited to 25 participants.
*Visions and Goals:* To provide an environment conducive to inner reflection and resonant with the simplicity and peace of oneness.

# The Gold Key Center and Sanctuary

3124 Central Avenue SE, Albuquerque, NM 87106
(505) 265-0008

*Hours:* 12:00 noon–3:00 p.m., Monday, Wednesday, and Friday

*Person to Contact:* Jaine R. Burgy, Director

*Founder/Owner:* Rothwell Lambe Camp (1972)

*Purpose:* To promote spiritual awareness in the community through classes, workshops, and seminars. Teachers and New Age leaders from throughout the nation and several foreign countries bring their information to us. We are also a metaphysical Christian church meeting in the Church of Malabar.

*Facilities:* A sanctuary/meeting room seating 50 people theatre style, a smaller room used for meditation, and an additional room which serves as our herb store.

*Services:* Metaphysically Christian-oriented church services on Sundays at 10:45 a.m., at the Church of Malabar. Workshops, seminars and classes in spiritual and new age subjects. Therapists include hypnotherapy, massage, and chromotherapy. Also work with radionics. Sponsors teachers, and lecturers from all over the country. In the past have sponsored Philippine psychic surgeons, healers who work with the etheric body. Sponsors Circles of Life Training, which is a whole brain technology. Run schools periodically; e.g., Dinshah chromotherapy. Training center for ministers and new age teachers. Offer an on-going class in "The Keys of Enoch" by Dr. J.J. Hurtak.

*Visions and Goals:* The Gold Key Center and Sanctuary will be the largest New Age Spiritual Center in the Southwest in 2 years, and the largest in the country in 5 years.

*Materials Available:* Bookstore. Herb store carrying Hanna Krager's herbal formulas and Sunrider regenerative herbs (which are a wholefood concentrate), as well as selling super bluegreen algae. Publish bimonthly newsletter. Publisher of "The New Age Source."

*Miscellaneous:* Our expansion will begin to take physical form in the first quarter of 1989.

# Rose Mountain Retreat Center

P.O. Box 355, Las Vegas, NM 87701
(505) 425-3144

*Hours:* Weeklong and weekend retreats, May–October
*Person to Contact:* Andy Gold, Director
*Founder:* Andy Gold ( April 1987)
*Owner:* Nonprofit/tax exempt
*Purpose:* The retreat center is dedicated to contributing toward the growth of peace and wisdom on our planet and beauty and balance within our hearts.
*Facilities:* We are an intertraditional retreat center located in an especially pristine and ecologically balanced section of the Sangre de Cristo Mountains, at an elevation of 8000 feet. The mountain itself is a most important teacher and nurturer. Residential programs with gourmet vegetarian meals. Our facilities are also available to ongoing groups whose visions overlap with our own.
*Services:* Moderately priced residential workshops in T'ai Chi, yoga, meditation, contemporary approaches in Judaism, Christianity, and Islam, Rites of Passage for adolescents and adults, holistic health, and self-awareness systems are offered annually.

# Ojo Caliente Mineral Springs

P.O. Box 468, Highway 414, Ojo Caliente, NM 87549
(505) 583-2233

*Hours:* Summer: 8:00 a.m.–8:00 p.m., 7 days a week. Winter: 1:00
   p.m.–8:00 p.m., Monday–Friday (Open at 8:00 a.m., Saturday and
   Sunday.)
*Person to Contact:* Viron Huff, President
*Founder:* Antonio Joseph ( early 1860s)
*Owner:* Ojo Caliente Mineral Springs Co.
*Purpose:* To provide an environment for people to relax and rejuvenate
   in natural hot mineral springs.
*Facilities:* Men's and women's bath houses, hotel-motel, and res-
   taurant.
*Services:* Hot mineral baths, massages, herbal wraps, and herbal
   facials.
*Visions and Goals:* To create a modern-day resort with turn-of-the-
   century charm.
*Miscellaneous:* The hot mineral water at Ojo Caliente has been used
   for many centuries, and it is believed that it has great healing
   powers.

# Cosmosis Radio

125 El Rancho Road North, Santa Fe, NM 87501
(505) 983-3059

*Hours:* Airs 8:00 a.m.–10:00 a.m., Sunday mornings on KLSK FM 104
*Person to Contact:* Alan or Luann Hutner, Hosts
*Founder/Owner:* Alan Hutner (February 1984)
*Purpose:* Cosmosis presents "new music" and conversations with
   guest experts about personal growth, human potential, conscious
   business, ecology, health, wellness, and social fissures of sig-
   nificance.
*Services:* The Cosmosis Community Calendar announces lectures,
   workshops, and activities locally, regionally, and nationally. Cosmosis features the latest in new music, including acoustic, electronic,
   new age, jazz, and vocals with lyrics containing messages of love and
   activism for positive social change. Guest interviews and call-in segments. We also sponsor a periodic Cosmosis Wilderness Wellness
   Weekend in the mountains of northern New Mexico as well as other
   retreats, workshops, and seminars in the Santa Fe area.
*Visions and Goals:* Cosmosis is considering national radio syndica-
   tion and is affiliated with Santa Fe Films, a film, television and
   video production company also working on a television show.

## GRD Health Clinic

301 E. Palace, Santa Fe, NM 87501
(505) 984-0934

*Hours:* 9:00 a.m.–6:00 p.m., Monday–Friday
*Founder/Owner:* Guruchander Singh Khalsa (January 1983)
*Purpose:* Diagnostic center for treatment and therapies for all disease processes. Practitioners give yoga therapy and meditations to enhance the healing process in a person's daily life.
*Facilities:* Outpatient clinic of 3,200 square feet.
*Services:* Chiropractic, acupuncture, physical therapy, naturopathy, massage therapy, counseling, nutritional counseling, and herbology.
*Visions and Goals:* National and international affiliations with other clinics.

## Nakée Healing Center

529 Old Santa Fe Trail, Santa Fe, NM 87501
(505) 986-0245

*Hours:* 10:00 a.m.–5:00 p.m., Monday–Saturday (open at 12:00 a.m. on Sunday)
*Founder/Owner:* Beverly and Nancy Shanklin (July 1988)
*Purpose:* A resource center for those looking to grow, heal, and evolve in the mind, body, and spirit and facilitate and guide all who come in the directions they need to travel.
*Facilities:* Small gem and mineral gallery that doubles up as a workshop and gathering space.
*Services:* A monthly itinerary of workshops and lectures from both local and national healers. In-house crystal healing, color therapy, massage, and channeling by appointment.
*Visions and Goals:* An unlimited national network of healing resources and dedication to helping all who are in need especially through referral.
*Materials Available:* Gems, minerals, crystals, jewelry, ceremonial drums, kiva ladders.

# NM Academy of Massage and Advanced Healing Arts
P.O. Box 932, Santa Fe, NM 87504
(505) 982-6271

*Hours:* 9:00 a.m.–5:00 p.m., Monday–Friday
*Person to Contact:* Dr. Robert March, Director
*Founder/Owner:* Dr. Robert March, ND (1981)
*Purpose:* To teach massage therapy and related healing arts. To operate a wellness clinic. Our specialty is vibrational healing. Using the principles of resonance, reinforcement, and interference in choosing vibrational remedies such as color, sound, homeopaths, herbs, gemstones, and flower remedies for balancing and harmonizing the mental, emotional, and physical energies of the client.
*Facilities:* School (4,500 sq. ft.) plus wellness center (1,000 sq. ft.).
*Services:* Massage, nutrition, herbology, acupressure, vibrational healing.
*Visions and Goals:* Healing of the individual and healing of the planet.

# The Life Center for Attitudinal Healing
P.O. Box 8718, Santa Fe, NM 87504
(505) 983-5541

*Hours:* 9:00 a.m.–5:00 p.m., Monday, Tuesday and Wednesday; 9:00 a.m.–3:00 p.m., Thursday; 9:00 a.m.–12:30 p.m., Friday
*Person to Contact:* Shelbee Matis, Executive Director
*Founder:* Marjorie Miller (1982)
*Owner:* Nonprofit organization
*Purpose:* Group and individual services for children and adults experiencing serious illness or loss. Attitudinal healing workshops for medical and social service professionals.
*Facilities:* Office.
*Services:* Weekly group and one-on-one at no charge. Presentations and workshops. Presentations by nationally known doctors and authors.
*Visions and Goals:* Training workshops for those in the medical and social services.
*Materials Available:* Books and tapes.

## SunRise Springs Resort

Route 14, Box 203, Santa Fe (La Cienega), NM 87505
(505) 471-3600/(800) 772-0500

*Hours:* 7:00 a.m.–11:00 p.m., 7 days a week
*Founder/Owner:* Megan Hill (1981)
*Purpose:* To nurture the body, rekindle the spirit, enhance creative
expression, and pursue the path of your own vision.
*Facilities:* A four-dimensional Living Center comprised of the Wellness Center, Accelerated Learning Forum, Botanical Gardens, and
the Vision Resource Center. New Garden Room accommodations,
heated swimming pool, hot tubs, and stone sweat lodge. Deva's garden shop, Merlin's Closet, the Crystal Room, the Inner Game Shop
and Sunrise 110. Lighted tennis courts, paved jogging/skating track,
and weight room. Natural food dining at Blue Heron Restaurant and
bar.
*Services:* A holistic array of massage, acupuncture, chiropractic, and
nutritional services. Classes in yoga, meditation, low-impact aerobics, and creative movement. Eight alpha chambers used for whole-
brain learning, stress reduction, and guided visualizations.
*Materials Available:* Natural fiber clothing, exercise clothes, rental
equipment, books, crystals, tapes, jewelry, musical instruments,
nutritional supplements, and wellness and body-care products.

# Women's Spiritual Center

P.O. Box 1831, Santa Fe, NM 87504
(505) 986-3499

*Hours:* 9:00 a.m.–5:00 p.m., Monday–Friday
*Person to Contact:* Sylvia Sedillo, Executive Director
*Founder/Owner:* Sylvia Sedillo and eight other women (November 1987)
*Purpose:* We are women of diverse cultures and beliefs who share our hopes, our needs, and our gifts. We provide a tranquil space for quiet prayer, reflection, solitude, and spiritual growth for women.
*Facilities:* We hold programs, retreats, and prayer/sharing in women's homes right now, but we are looking for a large house. This would have to be donated, as we cannot afford to buy or rent.
*Services:* Prayer groups, retreats, workshops, lectures, and sharing sessions. We operate by donations from foundations, groups, and individuals.
*Visions and Goals:* We envision a place where women can grow spiritually, discover the strengths within themselves, and find healing and joy in solitude and in companionship with other women. Once we have a house, we may operate a women's bed and breakfast in the summer to support our center.

# More Centers/Retreats

## Arizona
*Voyagers of Light*    1950 N. Arizona Ave., Suite 5, Chandler, AZ 85224 (602-899-3338)

*New World Educational Center*    5111 W. Maryland Avenue, Glendale, AZ 85301 (602-934-9931)

*Revis Mountain Self-Reliance School*    Box 1534, Globe, AZ 85501 (602-252-6019)

*Chevalier's Center*    4336 N. 7th Avenue, Phoenix, AZ 85013 (602-234-2090)

*International Holistic Center*    Box 15103, Phoenix, AZ 85060 (602-957-2181)

*Lukats Resort*    Route 1, Box 955, Safford, AZ 85546 (602-428-2881)

*The Sedona Institute*    2408 Arizona Biltmore Circle, #115, Phoenix, AZ 85016 (602-956-8766)

*Universariun Foundation Inc.*    Box 890, Taylor, AZ 85939 (602-536-7040)

*Rainbow Wellness Center*    2121 S. Mill Avenue, #225D, Tempe, AZ 85282 (602-968-5375)

*The Universal Life Alliance*    P.O. Box 27611, Tempe, AZ 85282 (602-894-6175)

*Brandlen Institute*    7161 N. Mona Lisa Road, Tucson, AZ 85741 (602-297-1207)

*Creative Consciousness Center*    5355 N. Hacienda Del Sol, Tucson, AZ 85718 (602-577-1757)

*Harmony & Health Foundation*    6535 E. Cloud Road, Tucson, AZ 85715 (602-881-7171)

## Colorado
*Gentle Reparenting Center*    Box 5531, Arvada, CO 80005 (303-422-0440)

*A Hero's Journey*    1047 Balsam Avenue, Boulder, CO 80302 (303-442-2088)

*Boulder Gestalt Institute*    5378 Sterling Drive, Boulder, CO 80301 (303-440-7490)

*Gold Lake Ranch*    2500 N. Broadway, Boulder, CO 80302 (303-444-1826)

*Hakomi Therapy*    Box 1873, Boulder, CO 80306 (303-443-6209)

*Image in Motion*    1085 14th Street, #1175, Boulder, CO 80302 (303-444-7926)

*Naropa Institute*    2130 Arapahoe Avenue, Boulder, CO 80302 (303-444-0202)

*Nyingma Institute of Colorado*    1441 Broadway, Boulder, CO 80302 (303-443-5550)

Personal Healing Institute   1113 Spruce, #301, Boulder, CO 80302
(303-449-0910)
Rocky Mountain Institute   1919 14th Street, #711, Boulder, CO
80302 (303-442-5373)
Colorado's Psychic Center   7352 N. Washington, Denver, CO 80229
(303-289-1117)
The Truth Center   4068 S. Broadway, Englewood, CO 80110
(303-789-4979)
Emissaries of Divine Light   Box 238, Loveland, CO 80537
Omega Foundation   P.O. Box 300, Loveland, CO 80537
(303-669-3336)
Whole Health Institute   4817 N. Country Road, Loveland, CO 80537
(303-679-4306)
Valley View Hot Springs   Box 175, Villa Grove, CO 81155

## Nevada
Association of Holistic Health Practitioners   3419 Thom Boulevard,
Las Vegas, NV 89106 (702-873-4542)

## New Mexico
Motivation Development Center   Box 25643, Albuquerque, NM
87125 (505-265-6557)
Center for Attitudinal Healing   P.O. Box 40162, Albuquerque, NM
87196 (505-884-9127)
Taeria Spiritual Community Foundation   Box 782, Carrizozo, NM
88301
Radium Springs Health Resort   Box 75, Radium Springs, NM 88054
Lama Foundation   Box 240, San Cristobal, NM 87564
(505-586-1269)
Friends of EKR   434 San Pasqual, Santa Fe, NM 87501 (505-984-1872)
Healing Arts of Santa Fe   Box 1445, Santa Fe, NM 87501
(505-988-4122)
Solar Vision   Box 431, Taos, NM 87571 (505-758-9761)
Charles Motel & Bathhouse   701 Broadway, Truth or Consequences,
NM 87901 (505-894-7154)

## Utah
Lamb-Lion Institute   1302 Yale Avenue, Salt Lake City, UT 84101
(801-582-0344)

# Part V: The Plains

# Evolutionary Education Foundation

5039 Outlook, Mission, KS 66202
(913) 432-0622

*Hours:* 9:00 a.m.–5:00 p.m., Monday–Friday
*Person to Contact:* David O'Quinn and Donna Buhrman
*Founder/Owner:* David O'Quinn and Donna Buhrman (1983)
*Purpose:* Created to serve spiritual eclectic healers, channels, teachers, and networkers in alignment with their divine and human selves.
*Facilities:* Seminars and private appointments held at 5039 Outlook. Our services are available to your area. Please send for sponsor information.
*Services:* Private readings, group channelings, healing of life and soul patterns, seminars.
*Visions and Goals:* As conscious channels and evolutionary educators, it is our mission to facilitate the awareness of the collective Christ consciousness upon this planet.
*Materials Available:* Books, tapes, written channelings, crystals, and stones.


# Shining Waters Ashram

Route 3, Box 560, Fredericktown, MO 63645
(314) 783-6715

*Hours:* 9:00 a.m.–5:00 p.m., Monday–Saturday
*Person to Contact:* Margie Arenivar, Administration
*Founder/Owner:* Universal Great Brotherhood (September 1983)
*Purpose:* To elevate the consciousness of the individual through interaction with others and nature, and to strengthen the individual by way of daily disciplines and abstinence from meat, tobacco, alcohol, drugs, coffee, and black tea.
*Facilities:* Dormitory space for 28, limited private dwellings when available, and unlimited camping on 40 acres of land in the Ozark mountains.
*Services:* Weekend workshops, opportunity to join the residents in daily disciplines of morning exercise, hatha yoga, and meditation. Openings available now for permanent and temporary residents.
*Visions and Goals:* To become self-sufficient, to allow residents a way to support themselves here. To create a functional community aspiring to the ideals of the Aquarian Age.

# Boulder Hot Springs

P.O. Box 1020, Boulder, MT 59632
(406) 225-4273

*Hours:* 9:00 a.m.–9:00 p.m., Sunday–Thursday; until 11:30 p.m., Friday and Saturday
*Person to Contact:* Bob Johnson, Manager
*Founder:* A.C. Quaintance (1880)
*Owner:* Time Zone Corporation
*Purpose:* To provide relaxation through our natural healing waters. Something about the property of the water, its temperature, its chemistry, relaxes the body, tones the muscles, and uplifts the spirit.
*Facilities:* Two hundred fifty acres of beautiful Montana mountain country. Hotel with 125 rooms, outdoor pool, two hot plunges, a cold plunge, two steam and shower rooms, lounge area with mini-bar/cafe, convention facilities, private meeting rooms, and central kitchen.
*Services:* Massage therapy, therapeutic mineral hot springs.
*Visions and Goals:* Better health through natural healing techniques.


# Feathered Pipe Ranch

Box 1682, Helena, MT 59624
(406) 442-8196

*Hours:* 9:00 a.m.–3:00 p.m., Monday–Friday
*Person to Contact:* India Supera, Director
*Founder/Owner:* India Supera (1975)
*Purpose:* To provide opportunities for people to envision and realize paths of growth leading toward personal and planetary transformation.
*Facilities:* Ranch with natural log and stone buildings, surrounded by national forest and wilderness. Tipis and yurts available. Sauna and hot tub, miles of hiking trails. Clean air and water.
*Services:* Daylong to weeklong educational seminars: yoga, dance, holistic health, shamanism, transpersonal psychology, massage. Community events:solstice gathering, concerts, ethnic dinners. We also feature world travel programs to places of pilgrimage such as Egypt, Greece, Peru, Mexico and Guatemala.
*Visions and Goals:* Personal and planetary transformation.

# Free Enterprise Health Mine

Box 67, Boulder, MT 59632
(406) 225-3383

*Hours:* 8:00 a.m.–8:00 p.m , 7 days a week. (Winter hours 8:00
a.m.–5:00 p.m.) Closed December, January, and February
*Person to Contact:* Bob and Peggy Johnson
*Founder:* Wade Lewis (1952)
*Owner:* Elkhorn Mining Company
*Purpose:* To provide relief from arthritis and other diseases by exposure
to carefully measured doses of radon. Similar mines and their
benefits are well known and well used in both Europe and the Soviet
Union.
*Facilities:* Mine tunnel and radon room.
*Visions and Goals:* To provide a natural treatment for arthritis and
assistance toward a pain-free life.
*Miscellaneous:* The Free Enterprise, Montana's first commercial ura-
nium mine, opened in 1949. Visitors soon began reporting relief
after going underground. Mining was stopped three years later and
Lewis, the founder and then president of Elkhorn Mining Co.,
opened a relatively spacious area 85 feet below the surface where
visitors could breathe the radon.

# More Centers/Retreats

**Missouri**
*Morning Glory Community*    2700 Oaker, Arnold, MO 63010
    (314-296-7846)
*Source-Life Enrichment Center*    2726 Ellendale, St. Louis, MO 63143
    (314-644-0641)
*Universal Great Brotherhood*    Solarline, Box 9154, St. Louis, MO
    63117

**Montana**
*Sleeping Child*    Box 1682, Hamilton, MT 59840 (406-363-6250)
*Friends of EKR*    P.O. Box 5872, Helena, MT 59604 (406-442-7811)
*Center for Attitudinal Healing*    200 Block E. Main, Missoula, MT
    59801 (406-728-2403)
*Terre de Lumiere Retreat*    Star Route, Box 1044, Roberts, MT 59070
    (800-342-2348)

**Nebraska**
*Human Development Network*    Box 24148, Omaha, NE 68124
    (402-390-0342)

# Part VI: The South

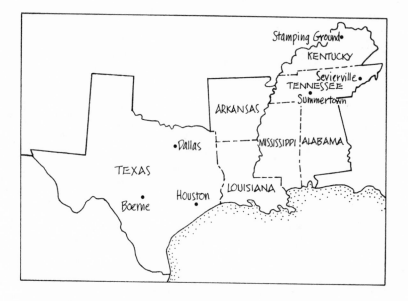

# Bluegrass Spa

901 Galloway Road, Stamping Ground, KY 40379
(502) 535-6261

*Hours:* 8:00 a.m.–10:00 p.m., 7 days a week
*Person to Contact:* Nancy Tazewell, Owner
*Founder:* Nancy Tazewell (1985)
*Purpose:* To introduce people to wholistic living and metaphysical awareness.
*Facilities:* Eight guest rooms, several meeting rooms, outdoor pool, sauna and jacuzzi, kitchen, dining room, massage and treatment rooms, exercise room, tennis court, golf course (adjoining), organic garden, and lake.
*Services:* Fitness program, workshops, lectures, and classes. Delicious and healthy natural foods. Massage, beauty, and body works.
*Visions and Goals:* To heighten awareness of who we are and how to accept our responsibilities in this life beginning with love.
*Materials Available:* Books, audiotapes and videotapes, clothes and gifts.

---

# The Farm

34, The Farm, Summertown, TN 38483
(615) 964-3574

*Hours:* 9:00 a.m.–3:00 p.m., Monday–Friday
*Founder/Owner:* Stephen Gaskin (1971)
*Purpose:* To promote peace, nonviolence, unity, and vegetarianism.
*Facilities:* Natural Rights Center, The Farm School, Store, Soy Dairy, Veggi-Deli, Dye Works, Book Co., Midwives Clinic, Solar Electronics, Tempeh Co., 1 World Trading Co., and Mail Order Co.
*Services:* Workshops can be arranged. Retreats and camping can also be set up. Kids-to-the-Country summers.
*Visions and Goals:* To continue striving for global harmony; to care for the land and each other.
*Materials Available:* Books, clothing, produce (in season), tapes, and vegetarian products.
*Miscellaneous:* The Farm still urges folks to support PLENTY, the relief organization that has brought help to Bangladesh, Guatemala, Jamaica, Dominica, Lesotho, the Bronx, and Pine Ridge. Their new address is: PLENTY USA, P.O. Box 2306, Davis, CA 95617-9961.

# Center for Peace

Route 11, Box 369, Sevierville, TN 37862
(615) 428-3595

*Hours:* 8:00 a.m.–7:00 p.m., 7 days a week
*Person to Contact:* Jean or Perry Robinson
*Founder/Owner:* Jean and Perry Robinson and Michael Hansen (December 1986)
*Purpose:* A place to learn and grow in communion with life: the New Age Church and Community, the Teaching and Healing Center, and the Woodland Mountain Resort and Campground.
*Facilities:* Natural forest/mountain setting, lodge and dining cabins, campground, swimming, hiking trails, library, and small bookstore.
*Services:* Sunday gathering, workshops, healing through crystals, therapeutic touch and herbs, counseling, hypnosis, and regression.
*Visions and Goals:* Personal, societal, and world healing. People living in loving/supportive groups. Expression of oneness of all life. The Center for Peace is nonsectarian, interdenominational and interfaith, focusing on truth that can be shared by all people rather than beliefs that tend to separate people.
*Materials Available:* Information sheets, workshop information, channeled writings, and tapes.

# Guadalupe River Ranch

P.O. Box 877, Boerne, TX 78006
(512) 537-4837

*Hours:* 24 hours a day, 7 days a week
*Person to Contact:* Jim Dixon
*Founder/Owner:* Walter Starcke (1977)
*Purpose:* The ideal balance of body, mind, and spirit is the heart of the Ranch experience. We strive to be a special environment where groups and individuals have the opportunity to design their own programs in a way that will achieve an unforgettable moment.
*Facilities:* Three hundred sixty acres with the Guadalupe River skirting the property. An 8,000-square-foot two-story main house provides space for socializing, meals, classes, and two conference rooms upstairs. Swimming pools, sauna, tennis and volleyball courts, Ping-Pong and pool tables, hiking trails, river tubing, and exercise equipment. Auditorium. Accommodations for up to 100 people.
*Services:* Aerobics and fitness classes, massage therapy, myotherapy, yoga, and other types of intensive muscular therapy.
*Visions and Goals:* Our goal is to provide a haven for those who want it all, a place where you can put mind, body, and spirit in harmony—and have a good time doing it.

## George Oshawa Macrobiotic Healing Center of Dallas

1507 N. Garrett Avenue, Dallas, TX 75206
(214) 821-6769

*Hours:* 8:00 a.m.–11:00 a.m./1:00 p.m.–5:00 p.m /7:00 p.m.–10:00 p.m., 7 days a week
*Person to Contact:* Francis Simun, Ph.D., Director
*Founder/Owner:* Francis Simun (1981)
*Purpose:* To provide macrobiotic aid and assistance for all those in need.
*Facilities:* Quiet rooms, restaurant, massage rooms, all types of supplies, and a park across the street for swimming, running, tennis, and volleyball.
*Services:* Dietary counseling, cooking school, shiatsu massage, gotai, and intellectual stimulation.
*Visions and Goals:* To provide an international retreat for anyone in need, regardless of race, color, or creed. A place for the weary to be rejuvenated in body, mind, and spirit, whether for an hour, a day, a week or a year.
*Materials Available:* Foodstuffs, hardware items for cooking, books, and magazines.

## Esoteric Philosophy Center

10450 Stancliff, Suite 100, Houston, TX 77099
(713) 561-9556

*Hours:* 9:00 a.m.–5:00 p.m , Monday–Friday
*Person to Contact:* Marian Smith
*Founder:* William David (1970)
*Owner:* Nonprofit school
*Purpose:* Personality integration for soul participation through the system of sound, color, and vibration.
*Facilities:* Classrooms, meeting room, bookstore, and library.
*Services:* Ongoing courses during the day and evening, lectures, workshops, and ceremonials.
*Visions and Goals:* Greater participation in world events from soul level. The healing of humanity.
*Materials Available:* Publishes *The Centric*, which can be obtained by subscription.

# Houston Center for Attitudinal Healing

2818 West T.C. Jester, Houston, TX 77018
(713) 688-1734

*Hours:* 9:00 a.m.–5:00 p.m., Monday–Friday
*Person to Contact:* Amy Bronstein, Director
*Founder:* Amy Bronstein (1983)
*Owner:* Nonprofit organization
*Purpose:* Emotional support for people experiencing catastrophic illness, loss of a loved one, or other life experiences requiring support.
*Facilities:* Remodeled house.
*Services:* We have groups for each member of the family—adults and children. Specific groups for those dealing with AIDS. Peer groups, person-to-person, and visitation. Workshops about attitudinal healing.
*Materials Available:* Books by Dr. Jampolsky, Course in Miracles books.

# Whispering Pines

114 Pine Grove Road, Scroggins, TX 75280
(214) 860-3326

*Hours:* 24 hours a day, 7 days a week
*Person to Contact:* Louise Curry, Manager
*Founder:* Gary Beavers ( March 1987)
*Owner:* Gary and Betty Beavers
*Purpose:* We are a community of families and individuals who have chosen to spend a segment of our lives together in a physical and spiritual environment that allows for and adds to our personal growth and understanding of ourselves and those who share in this great life journey. Some of us live at Whispering Pines seven days a week. Others come on weekends and whenever we have time to get out of the city. We have come here and remain here because we have discovered a unique place for teaching and learning of those truths that support the validity of life as an expression of love for ourselves and for the Source of our being.
*Facilities:* Forty-seven acres of pines, oaks, and dogwood trees, adjacent to Lake Cypress Springs near Mt. Vernon. Includes 9 acres of common area, a clubhouse, seminar building, library, bookstore, swimming pool, and 93 private lots with mobile homes. Some homes are in the rental pool and available as rentals to those visiting.
*Services:* We offer Saturday seminars, free to the public, and occasional fee-based seminars. Seminars include health, nutrition, wholistic health care, American Indian tradition, UFOs, music, neurolinguistic programming, yoga, and massage. Programs for both adults and teens on alcohol abuse and co-dependency and/or any other addictions.
*Visions and Goals:* We are to become a worldwide communications center for the purpose of presenting programs to the public without profit to the community, in an effort to educate the public with the knowledge and understanding that we create our own reality.
*Materials Available:* Books and tapes.

## More Centers/Retreats

### Alabama
*Alabama Center for Attitudinal Healing*   Box 39073, Birmingham, AL 35208 (205-786-9002)

### Arkansas
*Peacehaven*   P.O. Box 45, Deer, AR 72628 (501-446-5793)
*Evolutionary Education Foundation*   Box 34, Fayetteville, AR 72702
*Dimensions of Evolvement*   Star Route 3, Box 47, Melbourne, AR 72556 (501-368-4468)

### Texas
*Austin Area Holistic Health*   Box 13281, Austin, TX 78711 (512-472-9714)
*Austin Wellness Center*   5407B Clay Avenue, Austin, TX 78756 (512-451-6519)
*Center for Attitudinal Healing*   2755 Bee Cave Road, Austin, TX 78746 (512-327-1961)
*Center for Attitudinal Healing*   1017 S. Staples, Corpus Christi, TX 78404 (512-882-4820)
*Alphabiotic New Life Center*   2636 Walnut Hill Lane, #222, Dallas, TX 75206 (214-353-0563)
*The Shepherd's Bush Centre*   5416 Gaston Avenue, Dallas, TX 75214 (214-823-0292)
*Friends of EKR*   2309 Kingsway Drive, League City, TX 77573 (713-338-2439)
*Center for Attitudinal Healing*   911 Waterview Circle, Richardson, TX 75080 (214-727-1818)
*Pelly Health Farm*   Box 273, Weslaco, TX 78596 (512-968-5343)

# Part VII: The Midwest

# Spiritual Life Society and Yoga Center

1 E. Main Street (Old Church on the Green) Hudson, OH 44236
(216) 650-1216

*Founder:* Lawrence Terkel (1978)

*Owner:* Nonprofit organization

*Purpose:* To help people experience a spiritful life and promote a
healthful and meaningful relationship with themselves and others.

*Facilities:* All programs held in the serenity of the old church on the
green in the center of picturesque Hudson, Ohio. The church was
built in 1858.

*Services:* Sunday morning workshops, weekly yoga classes, nursery
school, interdenominational weddings, and other workshops.

*Materials Available:* Quarterly newsletter, lending library for
members.

# Oasis Center: New Horizons for Mind, Body, and Spirit

7463 North Sheridan Road, Chicago, IL 60626
(312) 274-6777

*Hours:* 10:00 a.m.–4:00 p.m., Monday–Friday
*Founder:* Robert B. Shapiro (1968)
*Owner:* Nonprofit/Board of Directors
*Purpose:* To provide an environment where people can involve themselves in various processes of personal development that may lead to more fulfilling lives and greater appreciation of human values as well as to provide training for individuals who desire to work with others toward this end. As an educational institution we are vitally interested in exploring the most effective ways of unlocking the dormant human potential in each of us. Our primary emphasis is not on teaching particular truths or techniques for daily life; rather our main concern is with a particular consciousness and with developing an environment to support the evolution of that consciousness—the consciousness of self-awareness/self-responsibility.
*Facilities:* Oasis Center is located in a house just south of Birchwood on the east side of the street.
*Services:* Oasis offers one-night introductory programs, no-registration drop-in events, one-day workshops, weekend workshops, weeklong workshops, and one-year or two-year training programs. Oasis programs vary from year to year, but we always present a wide variety oriented toward each of the three spheres of life: mind, body, and spirit.
*Visions and Goals:* We believe that the best potential for growth comes when a community of similarly motivated individuals come together to share what they know, rather than when one or a few charismatic individuals control the chain of communication.
*Miscellaneous:* Our high-quality/modest-cost tradition goes back to the beginning of Oasis when a dedicated body of famous early humanists including Alan Watts, Virginia Satir, and Fritz Perls agreed about the importance of spreading the best of the growth movement. We have added new leaders and lost old ones; today our best-known leaders still include Virginia Satir but now also Jean Houston, M. Scott Peck, and Shakti Gawain.

# Institute for Advanced Perception

719 S. Clarence Avenue, Oak Park, IL 60304
(312) 386-1742

*Hours:* 9:00 a.m.–5:00 p.m., Monday–Friday
*Person to Contact:* Donna Marie Schroeppel, President
*Founder:* Harold S. Schroeppel (May 1967)
*Owner:* Nonprofit corporation
*Purpose:* To teach psychic and spiritual development and consciousness-raising.
*Facilities:* Currently located in a house. Office, library, teaching rooms, use of kitchen. Several teachers at outlying locations: Hinsdale, Chicago, Villa Park, and Dayton, Ohio.
*Services:* Lectures and seminars, consultations, courses in self-awareness, classes in tarot, and correspondence courses.
*Visions and Goals:* To help create a better world by creating better people. Training teachers, developing more methods of following up on original lessons, developing communication points for graduates, and coordinating with other groups in the general area.

# Indianapolis Center for Attitudinal Healing

P.O. Box 55016, Indianapolis, IN 46205
(317) 251-5543

*Hours:* 9:00 a.m.–5:00 p.m., Monday–Friday
*Person to Contact:* Gerry Rhea
*Founder/Owner:* Gerry Rhea and William Griffith (December 1987)
*Purpose:* To provide free emotional support for families and individuals suffering from catastrophic disease and illness.
*Services:* Support groups, workshops, and community education.
*Visions and Goals:* To create a safe, unconditionally loving atmosphere to look at life and choose peace rather than conflict, love rather than fear.
*Materials Available:* Brochures and bookmarks.

# The Haven

Route 1, Box 57, Walkerville, MI 49459
(616) 898-2360 or 898-2974

*Hours:* 9:00 a.m.–10:00 p.m., 7 days a week
*Person to Contact:* Sharyn Roberts, Program Director
*Founder:* Al and Sharyn Roberts (1986)
*Owner:* Three Oaks Haven, Inc.
*Purpose:* Year-round spirit refuge for people who need space to grow, a created haven/protected place where there is time and space to reflect, share, and refresh in a setting close to nature. An affordable place where people can find the haven within themselves and go back to their daily work as protectors and meditators of that space within others they meet. Mind, body, and spirit seminars, seasonal celebrations, group and individual retreats in the healing environment.
*Facilities:* Two hundred ninety-five acres of beautiful woods and fields in the Manistee National Forest on crystal clear spring-fed lakes. Dormitories, log cabins, and tents. Meditation sites, fire circles, crystal shop, Dromenon sweat lodge. Glass-walled dining hall, smaller seminar rooms. Can accommodate 250 people. Skiing, swimming, boating, and hiking. Adjacent to 2,000 miles of national trails.
*Services:* Flexible conference and retreat services in a problem-free style for 8 to 260 people. Individual retreats with full meal service. Quiet individual and meditative spaces. Seminars and retreats featuring presenters from across the world. Schedule available quarterly. Adopt-an-Ace program. Not-for-profit research organization, Friends of the Haven, sponsors innovative teaching programs. Reiki therapists on site. Mini-seminars during summer months free to guests. Healing Arts Fesival in August.
*Visions and Goals:* A network of havens across the globe offering seminars, retreat space, and conferencing space in a healing environment close to nature.
*Materials Available:* Herb and crystal shop catalogs.

# *Center for Creative Learning*

777 W. Glencoe Place, Suite 200, Milwaukee, WI 53217
(414) 351-1633

*Hours:* 10:00 a.m.–7:00 p.m., Monday–Friday
*Person to Contact:* Steve Weliky, Manager
*Founder/Owner:* Patricia Durovy-Clason (June 1975)
*Purpose:* The Center for Creative Learning is a resource and training center for human potential development offering programs for personal and professional development.
*Facilities:* Course room and six offices including kids' room.
*Services:* Programming through the center includes business training (time management, communications, sales, etc.) and personal growth programs (seminars, workshops, and weekend intensives) as well as private consultations for personal and professional challenges.
*Visions and Goals:* To expand our programs nationwide. Make "Taking It Lightly" available in other centers internationally.
*Materials Available:* Books, cassettes, audio and video.

# Hidden Blessings

Street Address: 2650 Hamms Road, East Troy
Mailing Address: 5933 W. National Avenue, West Allis, WI 53214
(414) 259-1229

*Hours:* 9:00 a.m.–6:00 p.m., Monday–Friday
*Person to Contact:* Rosemarie H. Berres, Registrar
*Founder:* Rev. Thomas A. Sherbrook (July 1988)
*Owner:* Light-Streams, a nonprofit, nonsectarian religious organization
*Purpose:* Live-in retreats designed to be a life-changing, spiritual experience for those open to and searching for new meaning to life. Are you undergoing one of life's transitions: divorce? separation from a loved one? midlife career change? life-threatening disease? depression? recovery from rape or child abuse? bankruptcy? personal failure? change in life direction? If so, you'll want to learn more about a "Life-Changing" retreat at Hidden Blessings Retreat Center. In 2½ days as a part of a small group you will be given a plan of life that will help you reestablish your control over life's changing fortunes. You will be given powerful reasons for wanting to live, succeed, flourish, and prosper.
*Facilities:* Large, modern country estate surrounded by 17 acres of woods situated on 40 acres of private land. In-ground swimming pool.
*Services:* Once-a-month 3-day live-in retreats for up to 12 people. You will be shown how to overcome the disadvantages and failures of the past and turn them into advantages and successes. Meals included. Spiritual counseling and meditation training.
*Visions and Goals:* The primary goal is the emotional and spiritual healing of each individual and, in a larger sense, the healing of society. We will attempt by means of these retreats to return to individuals control over their lives and over the forces that mold them.
*Miscellaneous:* Over the ages man has learned ancient truths. Often hidden by powerful institutions, they can now be shared with you, entitling you to control your own destiny. Please write for more information.

# More Centers/Retreats

## Illinois

*Ravenest*  604 Mascontan Avenue, Belleville, IL 62220 (618-234-1727)

*The Focusing Institute*  410 S. Michigan Avenue, #212, Chicago, IL 60605

*Friends of EKR*  561 Dogwood Trail, Elk Grove Village, IL 60007 (312-437-4489)

*Fox Valley Gestalt Center*  1-30 W. State Street, Geneva, IL 60134 (312-232-1223)

*Wholistic Health Center*  137 S. Garfield Street, Hinsdale, IL 60521 (312-323-1920)

*Health Research Institute*  475 River Bend Road, #100, Naperville, IL 60540

*Friends of EKR*  P.O. Box 3696, Oakbrook, IL 60522 (312-990-0010)

## Iowa

*The Clearing*  1107 Clark Court, Iowa City, IA 52240 (319-337-5405)

## Michigan

*The Seva Foundation*  108 Spring Lake Drive, Chelsea, MI 48118

*Advancement of Natural Teachings*  16757 Linsay, Detroit, MI 48235 (313-837-8460)

*Beth El Holistic Awareness Center*  15769-75 E. Warren Avenue, Detroit, MI 48224 (313-331-5728)

*Center for Attitudinal Healing*  18300 Wildemere, Detroit, MI 48221 (313-861-1535)

*Primal Integration Center of Michigan*  23011 Middlebelt, Farmington Hills, MI 48024 (313-478-5559)

*Attitudinal Healing Center*  1145 Cambridge S.E., Grand Rapids, MI 49506 (616-245-3438)

*Kalamazoo Attitudinal Healing Center*  2601 Ricker, Richland, MI 49083 (616-375-7222)

*Gaylord Attitudinal Healing Center*  P.O. Box 271, Vanderbilt, MI 49795 (616-238-9541)

*United World Prosperity Corporation*  3275 Martin Road, Walled Lake, MI 48088 (313-669-2620)

**Minnesota**

*Center for Health Promotion*    2810 57th Avenue, #601, Brookdale
    Towers, MN 55430 (612-574-7800)
*Minnesota Center for Attitudinal Healing*    22020 Juniper Street
    N.W., Cedar, MN 55011 (612-753-2490)
*Present Moment*    3548 Grand Avenue S., Minneapolis, MN 55408
    (612-824-3157)
*Center for Holistic Healing*    569 Selby Avenue, St. Paul, MN 55102
    (612-291-7637)

**Ohio**

*Scott's Natural Health Institute*    Box 8919, Cleveland, OH 44136
    (216-238-6930)
*Rainbow Center for Attitudinal Healing*    P.O. Box 2802, Toledo, OH
    43606 (419-478-0202)

**Wisconsin**

*Inner Quest Journal*    Box 1162, Milwaukee, WI 53201
    (414-444-LOVE)
*New Frontiers Fellowship Farm*    Route 1, Oregon, WI 53575

# Part VIII: New England

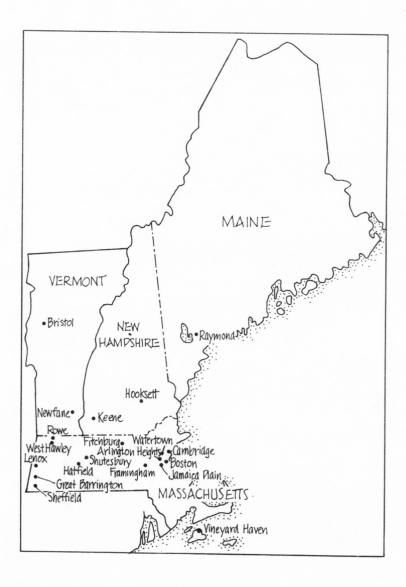

# Northern Pines

Route 85, R.R. Box 279, Raymond, ME 04071
(207) 655-7624

*Hours:* 8:30 a.m.–5:00 p.m.
*Founder/Owner:* Marlee and Pat Coughlan (1980)
*Purpose:* A healthy resort to help people get in touch with themselves. We will refresh your body and spirit with good food, exercise, serene surroundings, and friendly people.
*Facilities:* Our 80 acres of pine forests, rolling hills, and milelong waterfront offers the perfect place for a vacation. Accommodations range from lakeside log cabins of yesteryear to modern cottages and cabins and grand lodge with its double fireplaces and lakeside setting. Sauna and hot tubs. Flower and vegetable gardens.
*Services:* Exercise and fasting programs, massage, facials, aromatherapy, reflexology, hair treatments, and various forms of body work. Classes in cooking and various aspects of natural health. Programs often presented by special speakers. Canoes, rowboats, pedal boats, and sailboats available. Hiking, swimming, and jogging with cross-country skiing in the winter.
*Visions and Goals:* Helping you help yourself to better health, fitness, and energy.

# Sound Healers Association

P.O. Box 50, Arlington Heights, MA 02175
(617) 861-1625

*Hours:* 10:00 a.m.–6:00 p.m., Monday–Friday
*Person to Contact:* Jonathan S. Goldman, President
*Founder:* Jonathan S. Goldman (February 1982)
*Owner:* Nonprofit organization
*Purpose:* Sound Healers Association (SHA) is dedicated to research and education in the uses of sound and music for wellness.
*Facilities:* Meetings are held at a loft in Allston, Massachusetts, or at other locations depending on the size of the audience.
*Services:* Each month, SHA holds meetings that present guest speakers with various areas of expertise. SHA also sponsors the School of Sound, established in 1987 to teach the therapeutic use of sound, as well as workshops by our guest speakers when applicable.
*Miscellaneous:* Education: SHA disseminates information across the country. Networking: Working on a directory of Sound Healers throughout the U.S. Outreach: SHA promotes use of sound and music for wellness in hospitals. Resources: SHA publishes a monthly newsletter.

# Center for Well Being, Inc.

70 Bond Street, Fitchburg, MA 01420

(508) 345-5964

*Hours:* 10:00 a.m.–5:00 p.m., Tuesday–Friday

*Person to Contact:* Beatrice N. Niemi, Executive Director

*Founder:* Beatrice N. Niemi, M.A. (1982)

*Owner:* Nonprofit organization

*Purpose:* To foster growth of the individual in wholeness of body, mind, and spirit to encourage a higher level of wellness and well-being.

*Facilities:* Homelike atmosphere (but no overnight facilities).

*Services:* Programs and individual consultations in nutrition, counseling, touch for health, guided imagery and music, therapeutic touch and massage, facial rejuvenation, and official Reiki programs.

*Materials Available:* Allergy-free food supplements, water purifiers, vita-hites, informational handouts on related subjects, and a lending library of books and tapes.

# Ann Wigmore Foundation

(Division of Hippocrates Health Institute, Inc.)

196 Commonwealth Avenue, Boston, MA 02116

(617) 267-9424

*Hours:* 9:00 a.m.–4:00 p.m., 7 days a week

*Person to Contact:* C.J. Cosner, Administrator

*Founder:* Ann Wigmore, D.D., N.D. (1963)

*Purpose:* To sponsor research and education with an emphasis on the rehabilitation of health through the use of our Living Foods Lifestyle, as developed by Ann Wigmore, with emphasis on chlorophyll therapy.

*Services:* Two-week educational programs for resident students as well as workshop seminars conducted throughout the United States. Students are taught how to detoxify the body physically, mentally, emotionally, and spiritually and how to rebuild the health of the immune system.

*Visions and Goals:* To create a healthier and more enlightened society through a back-to-nature approach to living and the Living Foods Lifestyle.

*Materials Available:* Videos and manuals are available for those who wish to conduct their own workshops.

# The Center of the Light

P.O. Box 540, Great Barrington, MA 01230; or South Sandisfield Road, New Marlborough, MA
(413) 229-2396

*Hours:* 9:30 a.m.–8:00 p.m., Monday–Friday
*Person to Contact:* Staff
*Founder:* Eugene and Eva Graf and others (October 1979)
*Owner:* Church of Christ Consciousness (small, nondenominational, independent church)
*Purpose:* The Center of the Light is dedicated to the teaching and prospering of healing and spiritual growth, personal transformation, and responsible interaction with the planet. In all that we do, we strive to maintain a loving and supportive environment, one that nurtures the unique and emerging wholeness in each of us.
*Facilities:* Bordering on state forest, the center is located on 80 acres of orchards, lawns, and gardens as well as fields and woods. Several lakes are only minutes away. The center accommodates a maximum of 75 visitors at a time. We have chosen to keep the number of guests small to maintain the intimate, meditative quality inherent in the land. The Main House, a large concert barn, guest cabins, and other buildings accommodate the varied activities of the center, including the Center Bookstore and Cafe. Recreational facilities include a pool, a tennis court, ball field, and hiking trail. During the summer months, guests who would like to stay at the center without taking the program are welcome. The rustic, spiritually oriented setting is wonderfully suited to such quiet, personal vacation/retreat time.
*Services:* Staff and guest leaders facilitate workshops and programs covering a wide range of topics, from herbs to body work, from personal transformation to prayer. These workshops, which are experiential, practical, and informative, vary in length but are generally two to five days. In addition to the full summer schedule and the periodic workshops held throughout the year, several ongoing programs are offered at the center: the two-year Training for Healers program, the Herbal Apprenticeship Training, and the Facial Rejuvenation Certification program. The natural foods cuisine is delicious and abundant, oriented toward healing and primarily ovo-lacto-vegetarian.
*Visions and Goals:* To promote healing, and personal and spiritual growth as we can to anyone led to us. To continue to listen within so that we might be of service in the highest.
*Materials Available:* Newsletter (three to four times annually), books, and tapes.

# Ananda Healing Arts Center

1151 Massachusetts Avenue, Cambridge, MA 02139
(617) 492-3359

*Hours:* 8:00 a.m.–9:00 p.m., Monday–Friday
*Founder/Owner:* By a group (1972)
*Purpose:* The practice and teaching of healing arts.
*Facilities:* Four office rooms in a church setting.
*Services:* Professional certified practitioners specializing in the following areas of body work: Swedish Esalen massage, deep muscular
   massage, shiatsu/acupressure, polarity, structural deep tissue,
   perinatal massage, craniosacral, body awareness alignment, stress
   control and relaxation techniques, muscular therapy, and infant
   massage. Also our teaching staff offers in-depth massage training in
   beginning, intermediate, and advanced levels leading toward certification.
*Visions and Goals:* Integrate body, mind and spirit.
*Miscellaneous:* Gift certificates are available. Ananda is New
   England's oldest massage cooperative.


# Healers' Resource Center, Inc.

5 Upland Road (Porter Square), Cambridge, MA 02140
(617) 864-1989

*Hours:* 10:00 a.m.–6:00 p.m., Monday–Friday; 12:00 noon–6:00 p.m.,
   Saturday–Sunday
*Person to Contact:* Michele Robin Berg, Director
*Founder:* Chaya Sarah Sadeh, R.N., M.Ph. (1983)
*Owner:* Nonprofit organization
*Purpose:* To support the healing community through service. We offer
   an inexpensive, safe, supportive, and beautiful place to do your heal-
   ing work.
*Facilities:* A large remodeled apartment offering several wonderful
   rooms for rent to healers. Office is also bookstore and crystal store.
*Services:* Room rentals, information regarding health care and New
   Age events, ongoing classes, ongoing healing circles, special workshops, Healing Fairs every Saturday and Sunday from 12:00 noon to
   6:00 p.m., with psychic reading and body work healings available,
   and a referral service.
*Visions and Goals:* To encourage healing throughout the planet by
   creating and supporting community on a local level.
*Materials Available:* Books, crystals, organic herbs, crafts/artwork.

# Spring Hill of Ashby Inc.

675 Massachusetts Avenue, Cambridge, MA 02139
(617) 864-9181

*Hours:* 9:00 a.m.–5:00 p.m., Monday–Friday
*Founder:* Robert and Judith Gass (early 1970s)
*Owner:* Nonprofit
*Purpose:* Spring Hill is a place, a community of spirit, and an organization that offers the Opening the Heart workshops, trainings, and other programs in what we call the Heart-Centered Approach to therapy and healing. Our approach to personal growth and healing emphasizes love, service, and "being in touch" rather than technique. It utilizes many different avenues to the human heart, which is the source of healing and the key to transformation.
*Facilities:* On our 80 acres we have hiking trails, a sweat lodge, gift shop, our conference center "barn," and a large farmhouse.
*Services:* Opening the Heart workshops for individuals and couples; specialty heart workshops, daylong workshops; special events, celebrations, and training programs.
*Materials Available:* Crystals, crystal jewelry, note cards, books and other publications, tapes and clothing, and other beautiful and healing gifts.

# Center for Holistic Health

42 Lincoln Street, Framingham, MA 01701
(508) 879-3002

*Hours:* 9:00 a.m.–7:00 p.m., Monday–Friday; 9:00 a.m.–1:00 p.m., Saturday
*Person to Contact:* Reception
*Founder/Owner:* John Myersom, Lic.Ac., and Dennis Reynolds, Lic.Ac., Ph.D., Directors (1977)
*Purpose:* To make people feel better. We deal directly with the physical and emotional cause of your complaint—not just the symptoms— by restoring your body's own natural energetic balance.
*Facilities:* An old Victorian house in downtown Framingham.
*Services:* Classes, seminars, and trainings that put you in charge of your physical, emotional, and spiritual health; for example, stress management, yoga, tarot, Tai Chi Ch'uan, Shen Tao sword, calligraphy, and Zen meditation. A variety of treatments, all relying on your body's natural internal healing ability and avoiding synthetic drugs or medications; for example, acupuncture, counseling and psychotherapy, herbal therapy, nutrition, and therapeutic massage (Swedish, acupressure/shiatsu, polarity, deep breathing, and movement therapy).

# Stillpoint School of Massage and Center for the Healing Arts

P.O. Box 15, 60 Main Street, Hatfield, MA 01038
(413) 9322

*Hours:* 9:00 a.m.–5:00 p.m., Monday–Friday

*Founder/Owner:* Not applicable

*Purpose:* To provide holistic training in massage therapy and related healing arts. At the heart of our program is "massage with a conscious- ness." We believe it is not enough to learn a sequence of strokes, pressure points, or other techniques; not enough to have factual knowledge about the human body, its structures, its functions, and so forth. We believe that while such knowledge and skills are absolutely essential, the level of awareness of the practitioner is equally important.

This refers to the degree to which the massage therapist is "clear" and "centered" and thus better able to be of service to others and promote their healing and well-being. To get to such a place, one must work at removing the obstacles to one's own physical, emotional, and spiritual well-being, including negative thoughts and attitudes, health-destructive habits, relationships, and life-styles, unresolved conflicts, and physical and emotional traumas stored in the body.

At Stillpoint, this process is facilitated by a very supportive community and by specific courses including Personal Awareness and Growth, Counseling and Communication Skills, Wholistic Health, Meditation, Visualization and Imagery in Healing, and Yoga. Stillpoint thus combines sound vocational training in massage therapy with opportunities for significant personal transformation and growth, which together form a solid foundation for a satisfying and rewarding career in the healing arts.

*Facilities:* Classrooms, clinic, and office in a spacious building located on a beautiful site along the Connecticut River, with inspiring views of surrounding valley farmland.

*Services:* Full-time and part-time, day and evening certification programs in massage therapy, approved by the American Massage Therapy Association. Also, continuing and community education classes and workshops in the areas of personal/spiritual awareness and growth, body-work, and related healing arts.

*Materials Available:* Distributor of quality massage tables.

# New Life Health Center

12 Harris Avenue, Jamaica Plain, MA 02130
(617) 524-9551

*Hours:* 8:00 a.m.–8:00 p.m , 7 days a week
*Person to Contact:* Carol Thompson, Administrative Assistant
*Founder/Owner:* Bo-In Lee (1977)
*Purpose:* To promote the total health of the individual—physical, emotional, psychological, and spiritual—through guided self-healing. Also, thereby to contribute to the healing of society and of the planet itself.
*Facilities:* A spacious 3-story building two blocks from scenic Jamaica Pond, Boston. This contains a yoga and exercise hall, a lecture room, a dining room and natural foods kitchen, a physical therapy room, an acupuncture treatment room, Oriental herb room, sauna, and 12 bedrooms for guests.
*Services:* Ongoing classes in natural foods diet and cookery, yoga, relaxation and visualization techniques, and meditation. Noninvasive therapeutic treatments including acupuncture, acupressure massage, moxabustion, cupping, Oriental herbs, corrective exercises, and psychomatic and emotional counseling. A 21-day healing and rejuvenative "New Life" program. This residential experience combines classes, daily therapeutic treatments, and for most participants a 7 to 10-day cleansing fast. Weight-loss and natural pregnancy counseling. Self-realization workshops. Acupuncture Healing Arts Program, which involves instructional and apprentice elements and which can lead to licensing.
*Visions and Goals:* We hope to combine the best aspects of Oriental medicine with the best aspects of Western medicine, and create a synthesis that will benefit all humanity.
*Miscellaneous:* Bo-In Lee, a native of Korea, is an Oriental healer who has been studying and practicing the healing arts of East and West for over twenty-five years. He is a licensed acupuncturist and herbalist and is a Master of Yoga, Zen meditation, and several martial arts.

## Foxhollow Wellness Spa

Route 7, Lenox, MA 01240
(413) 637-2000

*Hours:* 9:00 a.m.–5:00 p.m., Monday–Friday
*Person to Contact:* Sara Schley, Marketing Director
*Founder:* Stephan Rechtschaffen, M.D. (spring 1988)
*Owner:* Donald Altschuler and Stephan Rechtschaffen, in partnership
*Purpose:* Health promotion programs to maximize renewal, rejuvenation, and optimal well-being.
*Facilities:* Exercise equipment, flotation tanks, swimming pool, jacuzzi, tennis, horseback riding, cross country skiing in winter, and a natural gourmet cuisine.
*Services:* Massage, herbal wraps, and aerobics. Other programs offered in conjunction with the Omega Institute, Rhinebeck, New York.

## Kripalu Center for Yoga and Health

P.O. Box 793, Lenox, MA 01240
(413) 637-3280

*Hours:* 8:30 a.m.–5:00 p.m., Monday–Saturday
*Person to Contact:* Barbara Nelson (Suniti), Program Support Staff Manager
*Founder:* Yogi Amrit Desai (1971)
*Owner:* Nonprofit organization owned and run by volunteer residential staff
*Purpose:* Self-discovery through holistic health and yoga. Kripali Center is truly holistic, treating each person as a whole being and recognizing the essential unity of body, mind, and spirit.
*Facilities:* Accommodations in one building , dining chapel offering extensive vegetarian buffet, saunas, whirlpools, lakefront with swimming and extensive hiking trails.
*Services:* Residential programs ranging from 2 to 27 nights in health, personal growth, and yoga related subjects. Monthlong certified professional programs in yoga teachers' training and body work. Health services include body work, polarity, shiatsu, yoga therapy.
*Materials Available:* Bookstore, wellness and body care supplies, crystals, tapes, videos, and clothing.

# Rowe Camp and Conference Center

Kings Highway Road, Rowe, MA 01367
(413) 339-4216

*Hours:* 9:30 a.m.–6:00 p.m., Monday–Friday
*Founder:* Unitarians founded the camp in 1924; Doug Wilson founded the conference center in 1974
*Owner:* Nonprofit organization
*Purpose:* Personal growth, healing, and change in the context of a supportive community that also seeks to heal the earth.
*Facilities:* Seventeen buildings, including a sauna, the Orchard Guest House and Farmhouse, and a large meeting room in the recreation hall. Accommodations for 120, surrounded by 1,400 acres "held in trust forever wild."
*Services:* In the fall, winter, and spring we offer weekend retreats for adults and families. Summers, we are a camp for young people 8 to 18, women, adults, and families. We serve gourmet vegetarian food.
*Visions and Goals:* We seek to offer a warm, nurturing, wholesome, lively place where people can reflect on their lives, deepen their feelings, reach out to others, and return to their regular lives revitalized.

# Sirius Community

Baker Road, Shutesbury, MA 01072
(413) 259-1251

*Hours:* 9:00 a.m.–9:00 p.m., Monday–Friday
*Person to Contact:* Paul Miksis, Guest Coordinator
*Founder:* Corinne McLaughlin and Gordon Davidson (September 1978)
*Owner:* Nonprofit corporation (educational)
*Purpose:* To help the spiritual growth of members and visitors through daily living, educational programs, and spiritual practices; to live a healthier life-style close to the earth and in harmony with God and each other.
*Facilities:* Several community houses, community center, guest accommodations, classroom, meditation room, library, pond, community garden, and sweat lodge.
*Services:* Classes in spiritual growth, meditation, wholistic health, organic gardening, solar building; community living experiences; 9-month course in Spiritual Science; counseling; massage; Sunday services; daily group meditation; earth ceremonies; credit courses through University of Massachusetts.

# The Option Institute & Fellowship— "A Place for Miracles"

RD #1, Box 174A, Sheffield, MA 01257
(413) 229-2100

*Hours:* 8:30 a.m.–5:30 p.m., Monday–Friday
*Person to Contact:* Carol Wertz, Program Direction
*Founder:* Barry Neil Kaufman and Suzi Lyte Kaufman (1983)
*Owner:* A federally nonprofit, education organization
*Purpose:* Our purpose is to live and teach a most remarkable perspective and method, the Option Process, which is based on an attitude of unconditional love and acceptance. The Option Process is an educational tool that allows each individual to experience a greater happiness along with the power, clarity, and healing that accompany it.
*Facilities:* Eighty-five mountainside acres in western Massachusetts' Berkshire hills including comfortable, new and aesthetically pleasing guest houses, sweeping lawns, forests, waterfalls, and magnificent views. Our property has direct access to the Appalachian Trail and to a wide range of cultural and recreational activities.
*Services:* Group programs on a year-round basis varying in length from weekends to 8 weeks. Programs include topics such as relationships, parenting, and empowering yourself. Also offered are private counseling sessions for adults, children, couples, and families. Additionally, we offer the acclaimed and highly successful Option Program for "special" children (autistic, brain impaired, learning disabled, cerebral palsy, etc.) and their families.
*Visions and Goals:* To the best of our capacity, we strive to be a real "Place for Miracles," a place of hope and possibility for many who are without hope, a place for others whose difficulties seem irreversible to experience healing, and a place where each individual is embraced and celebrated for his or her uniqueness.
*Materials Available:* Books and tapes about the Option Process by Barry Neil Kaufman, including the best-selling "Son Rise," "Giant Steps," "To Love is to be Happy," "A Miracle to Believe In," and others. Also available for loan is the award-winning NBC-TV movie "Son-Rise: A Miracle of Love," which describes the Kaufman's successful work with their once-autistic child.

# Body and Soul

RFD 611, Vineyard Haven, MA 02568
(508) 693-6460

*Hours:* 9:00 a.m.–6:00 p.m., 7 days a week
*Person to Contact:* Eva Brenish or Neila Hoffman
*Founder:* Jackie Entwhistle (1980)
*Owner:* Neila Hoffman and Eva Brenish
*Purpose:* A holistically oriented center for therapeutic relaxation, healing, and self-care.
*Services:* Therapeutic massage, sports massage, and herbal facials. Weekly classes in massage.
*Visions and Goals:* Eva Brenish and Neila Hoffman recently took over Body and Soul from Jackie Entwhistle, who has gone on to form a center for classes and individual work for exploring and integrating the body, emotions, creativity, spirit and movement. (She can be reached at 508-693-7258.) Eva and Neila envision creating with Body and Soul a more extensive healing arts center, to be involved with other practitioners, to offer workshops, and to install a hot tub.
*Materials Available:* Holistic bookstore, Bach remedies, crystal specimens, and Dr. Christopher herbal supplies.

# Turning Point (Family Wellness Center)

173 Mount Auburn Street, Watertown, MA 02172
(617) 923-4604/6

*Hours:* 9:00 a.m.– 5:00 p.m., Monday–Friday (Evenings, 924-6040)
*Person to Contact:* Dolores Heeb, Registered Acupuncturist
*Founder/Owner:* Richard Ingrasci, M.D., M.P.H., Richard Moskowitz, M.D., Ted Chapman, M.D., Geri Schumacher, R.N., and Dolores Heeb, Lic.Ac., B.Ac., (1983)
*Purpose:* To offer a friendly, supportive environment in which people are encouraged to take personal responsibility for their health. Our work is rooted in noninvasive, nontoxic approaches that stimulate the innate capacity for self-healing.
*Facilities:* Office building just east of Watertown Square.
*Services:* Family practice medicine, classical homeopathy, traditional acupuncture, psychotherapy, psychospiritual healing groups, cancer counseling, nutritional counseling, and body-oriented therapies.
*Visions and Goals:* To provide comprehensive care for the health-related needs of families and individuals from serious illness to high-level wellness.

# Interface

P.O. Box 860, 552 Main Street, Watertown, MA 02172
(617) 924-1100

*Hours:* 10:00 a.m.–5:00 p.m., Monday–Friday
*Person to Contact:* Miki Boni, Registrar
*Founder/Owner:* Coalition of physicians and health professionals (1975)
*Purpose:* To explore those trends in health, personal growth, science,
and religion which excite and encourage us to seek new ways of living, expand personal horizons, and join with others to help create a
better world. Our focus is on health for the whole person—body,
mind, and spirit.
*Facilities:* Classrooms, auditorium, and bookstore located in a relaxed
and welcoming environment.
*Services:* Lectures, courses, and workshops presented by an international faculty in a variety of subjects including health and healing,
relationships and family, professional development, and psychology
and personal growth. Produce over 200 courses per semester including evening talks and retreats.

Some examples of workshops offered are "The Further Reaches of
Human Energy" with George Leonard and Annie Styron Leonard; "A
New Kind of Prosperity for the 80s" with Ruth Ross, Ph.D.; "A Day
for Men" with Robert Bly; "Thinking Aloud" with Abbie Hoffman;
"Opening the Heart" with Robert Gass, Ed.D.; "Creation Spiritual-
ity" with Matthew Fox, O.P.; "Change Your Mind, Change Your Life"
with Gerald Jampolsky, M.D., and Diane V. Cirincione; and "The
Psychology of Illness and the Art of Healing" with Bernard Siegel,
M.D., and Barbara Siegel, B.S.

Some examples of evening talks offered are: "The Goddess and
Evolution" with Merlin Stone; "Transformational Medicine" with
Leonard Laskow, M.D.; and "Radiant Relationship" with Richard
Moss, M.D.

Examples of retreats offered are "The Courage to Heal: A Retreat
for Women Survivors of Child Abuse" with Ellen Bass, held at the
Essex Retreat Center in Essex, Massachusetts; and "Christian Mysti-
cism" with Bruce Davis, Ph.D., held at the Briarwood Conference
Center in Monument Beach, Massachusetts.
*Visions and Goals:* Our goal is to offer a safe place for inner work,
inquiry, discovery, and the practice of life-enhancing habits.
*Miscellaneous:* On most weekends, we have reasonably priced lunches
provided on campus by Taha Natural Foods of Cambridge. There is
no lodging available at the Interface Center, but we have a list of
hotels, motels, and bed and breakfasts located within a 10- to
20-mile radius of the center which we can send to you.

# Stump Sprouts Lodge, X-Country Ski Center

West Hill Road, West Hawley, MA 01339
(413) 339-4265

*Hours:* 9:00 a.m.–5:00 p.m., Monday–Friday
*Person to Contact:* Lloyd or Suzanne Crawford, Owners
*Founder/Owner:* Lloyd and Suzanne Crawford (1977)
*Purpose:* Retreat center for people to meet new friends, feel the freedom of wide open space, and recharge the soul.
*Facilities:* A new guest lodge, a farmhouse, a couple of old barns, and a few goats and chickens make up our homestead, along with an outdoor wood-fired sauna and recreation room, all situated high on the side of a mountain with a magnificent view. Tract of 450 acres surrounded by state forest. Several cozy bunkrooms that sleep 2 to 8 people.
*Services:* Cross-country skiing instruction. Hearty home-cooked family-style meals with food from our garden whenever possible.
*Visions and Goals:* Create a relaxed informal setting for individuals and groups, with a "homemade" feel.
*Materials Available:* Cross-country ski equipment for rent.

# Earthstar: The Observatory of the Inner Self

50 Whitehall Road, Hooksett, NH 03106
(603) 669-9497

*Hours:* 1:00 p.m.–9:00 p.m, Monday–Friday; 11:00 a.m.–6:00 p.m., Saturday
*Person to Contact:* DyJahna or Saryna, Co-managers
*Founder:* Kamala Renner (1973)
*Owner:* Kamala and Jack Renner
*Purpose:* Observatory of the inner self focusing on personal growth and stress reduction education.
*Facilities:* Converted farm house with guest rooms, massage rooms, gift shop, sauna, and heated pool on 8 acres of land in a magical otherworldly atmosphere.
*Services:* Kriya massage, alchemia, rebirthing, yoga, Reiki, acupressure, astrology, alchemical counseling, colonics, and fasting.
*Visions and Goals:* Peace and harmony personally and then collectively for a complete healing of the planet.
*Materials Available:* Crystals, New Age jewelry, metaphysical books, New Age tapes, and massage supplies.

# The Next Step, Inc.

16 Church Street, Keene, NH 03431
(603) 357-0744

*Hours:* 9:00 a.m.–5:30 p.m., Monday–Friday
*Person to Contact:* Paula Hanrahan, President
*Founders/Owners:* Sheila Simon, Heather Krachey, Nancy Bradley,
  Paula Hanrahan, and Michael Hanrahan (April 1987)
*Purpose:* We provide therapeutic and educational services to facilitate
  personal growth and to promote health of body, mind, and spirit.
*Facilities:* Four practitioners' offices, classroom.
*Services:* Body-centered therapies: massage, polarity, shiatsu, etheric
  bodywork, yoga, therapeutic touch, reflexology, spiritual counsel-
  ing. Classes and workshops.
*Visions and Goals:* To raise consciousness in the community and edu-
  cate community about holistic health.
*Materials Available:* Books and tapes related to personal growth.


# Sunray Meditation Society

P.O. Box 308, Bristol, VT 05443
(802) 453-4610

*Hours:* 9:30 a.m.–5:30 p.m., Monday–Friday
*Person to Contact:* Jemsa Sheriff, Office Manager
*Founder/Owner:* The Venerable Ugvwiyihi Dhyani Ywahoo (1968)
*Purpose:* An international spiritual society dedicated to planetary
  peace. Its purpose is to manifest the Native American ideal of
  Caretaker Mind, that we may create a world of beauty on Earth and
  throughout the family of life.
*Facilities:* The Sunray Peace Village Encampment, an outdoor community based on traditional Cherokee principles, where programs
  are offered in the summer. Sunray International headquarters and
  administrative offices.
*Services:* Through the Peacemaker Mission, a yearly program offered
  regionally in North America and Europe, and other educational programs, the teachings of the Ywahoo Lineage and the Dharma are
  brought to individuals and communities throughout the planet.
*Materials Available:* Sunray tapes and literature including Dhyani
  Ywahoo's "Voices of Our Ancestors: Cherokee Teachings from the
  Wisdom Fire."

# Heart's Bend

P.O. Box 217, Newfane, VT 05345
(802) 365-7616

*Person to Contact:* Dr. Nina Lynn, Director
*Founder/Owner:* Dr. Nina Lynn (1970)
*Purpose:* A "home away from home." Inspired by educational idealism, Nina eagerly opens her home and her heart to the "many'"—trusting in children, learning, loving life, giving others a chance to do the same.
*Facilities:* One hundred hillside acres of woods and open fields include a tennis court, brook-fed swimming pond, and an amphitheater. Accommodations include Dr. Lynn's home, the Pondhouse, the Cabin, the Hideaway, the Studio, the "Sanderson House," and the lean-to area.
*Services:* A children's community, Heart's Bend offers Summer Farm Camp, a six week co-ed program for 65 young people, ages 4-15; Focus Camps, a two-week program for campers to concentrate on specific skills in drama, art, cooking, outdoor adventure, or horsemanship; Switzerland, a program limited to 12 participants in which the group flies to Zurich; retreat weekend, which is designed to enable each participant to cultivate an honest self-image and positive sense of personal worth.

## More Centers/Retreats

**Maine**

*Friends of EKR*    34 Clifford Street, Mechanic Falls, ME 04256
(207-345-9873)

**Massachusetts**

*Synthesis Center*    Box 575, Amherst, MA 01004 (413-256-0772)

*The Light Ages Foundation*    Box 278, Ashfield, MA 01330

*Beacon Hill Health Association*    14 Beacon Street, #620, Boston, MA
02108 (617-523-8017)

*East/West Foundation*    17 Station Street, Boston, MA 02138
(617-738-0045)

*The Outreach Institute*    Kenmore Station, Box 368, Boston, MA
02215

*Aqua Retreat Center*    214 Market Street, Brighton, MA 02135
(617-787-3511)

*The Kushi Foundation*    17 Station Street, Box 1100, Brookline, MA
02147 (617-738-0045)

*Cambridge Holistic Health Center*    2557 Massachusetts Avenue,
Cambridge, MA 02140 (617-661-6225)

*Prosper!*    Box 134, Cambridge, MA 02140 (617-497-8280)

*Woolman Hill Conference Center*    Keets Road, Deerfield, MA 01342
(413-774-3431)

*Essex Retreat Center*    Conomo Point Road, Essex, MA 01929
(617-768-7374)

*Three Mountain Foundation*    59 Commonwealth Avenue, Haverhill,
MA 01830 (617-372-5119)

*Heartspring Health Center*    52 Hempstead Road, Jamaica Plain, MA
02130 (617-738-4366)

*Friends of EKR*    15 Parkinson Street, Needham, MA 02192
(617-444-7977)

*Silent Meditation Retreat*    Box 51BB, Shelbourne Falls, MA 01370
(413-625-9228)

*Trusteeship Institute*    Baker Road, Shutesbury, MA 01072
(413-253-7500)

*K.C. & Company*    386 LaGrange Street, West Roxbury, MA 02132
(617-469-4700)

**New Hampshire**

*Another Place*   Route 123, Greenville, NH 03048 (603-878-1510)

**Vermont**

*Cooper Hill Inn*   P.O. Box 146, E. Dover, VT 05341 (802-348-6333)
*New Life Health Spa*   Liftline Lodge, Stratton Mountain, VT 05155 (802-297-2534)
*Plum Creek*   Box 82A, Waitsfield, VT 05673 (802-496-3262)

# Part IX: The Mid-Atlantic

NEW YORK

Sharon Springs

Roscoe • Woodstock

CONNECTICUT   R.I.

Neversink • Rhinebeck

Honesdale •   • Woodbury

• Nyack   Darien

Paramus •   • Rye

New York City •   Manhasset

• Brooklyn

PENNSYLVANIA

Spring House

Plymouth Meeting •   • Philadelphia

MARYLAND   NEW JERSEY

Chevy Chase   Bethesda
Washington, D.C.   Silver Spring   DEL.

# Center for Hope, Inc.

374 Middlesex Road, Darien, CT 06820
(203) 655-4693

*Hours:* 8:30 a.m.–5:00 p.m., Monday–Friday
*Person to Contact:* Patricia Boyle, Executive Director
*Founder:* Mary Anne Marion (1982)
*Owner:* Nonprofit organization
*Purpose:* To offer support services for adults and children with life-threatening illnesses, families with seriously ill members, and the bereaved.
*Facilities:* On-site space available for children and adults.
*Services:* Support groups for adults and children as noted above. Individual consultation, educational materials.
*Materials Available:* Library of books, videos, tapes, and audiotapes. Toys and materials available for work with children.

# Woodbury Yoga Center

122 West Side Road, Woodbury, CT 06798
(203) 263-2254

*Hours:* 10:00 a.m.–10:00 p.m., Monday–Friday
*Person to Contact:* Janaki Pievson or Tom Thompson, Owners
*Founder/Owners:* Janaki Pievson and Tom Thompson (1981)
*Purpose:* To thoroughly train people in the enlightenment tradition of yoga and provide a center and community to manifest this.
*Facilities:* Located on 38 acres of field, a meditation hall, library, bookstore, classrooms, meditation room and Hatha yoga room.
*Services:* Trainings in all aspects of yoga, meditation and spiritual life through classes, free meditation programs and private sessions. We offer workshops and seminars on the yoga of death and dying, stress management, Hara training, getting out of your way and allowing life to work, and the foundations of meditation and Hatha yoga.
*Visions and Goals:* To awaken people to their true self and true potential on a physical, mental, psychic, and spiritual level. Our motto is "Inner peace is World peace."

# Shanti Yoga—Center for Harmony

4325 East-West Highway, Bethesda, MD 20814
(202) 362-2656

*Hours:* 9:00 a.m.–9:00 p.m., 7 days a week
*Person to Contact:* Vyasa
*Founder/Owner:* Vyasa (1985)
*Purpose:* Instruction on and services for holistic health. Shanti is the Sanskrit word for peace and yoga is the practice or set of practices for self-realization. Therefore, Shanti Yoga can be interpreted as the search for peace through self-realization.
*Facilities:* Small intimate house, short- and long-term accommodations.
*Services:* Ongoing beginner, intermediate, and advanced Hatha yoga, meditation, and Raja yoga classes. Optional daily practices beginning at 5:00 a.m., weekend workshops and retreats (individual retreats available), and ongoing deep muscle therapy and acupuncture treatment. In addition, tea ceremonies, classes in Japanese and Chinese vegetarian cooking, stress management, nutrition, biofeedback, and weight control.
*Materials Available:* Small shop with books, tapes, crystals, and so forth.

# Unity Woods Yoga Center

4853 Cordell Avenue, Suite 300, Bethesda, MD 20814
(301) 656-8992

*Hours:* 9:00 a.m.–5:00 p.m., Monday–Friday
*Person to Contact:* Esther Geiger, Administrative Assistant
*Founder/Owner:* John Schumacher (1973)
*Purpose:* To bring you the finest yoga instruction. We conduct classes for all levels of students in asana (posture) and pranayama (breathing) as well as present workshops with some of the finest teachers from all over the world, weekend intensives, and a wide-ranging program of seminars covering various aspects of the science and art of yoga.
*Facilities:* Yoga studio.
*Services:* Classes in Hatha yoga, yoga philosophy, meditation and breathing, guest instructors, private therapeutic instruction, workshops, and intensives conducted throughout the United States.
*Visions and Goals:* Save the world.
*Materials available:* The Beyondananda Boutique selling accoutrements for the yoga practitioner, through either direct sales or mail order.

# Common Boundary

7005 Florida Street, Chevy Chase, MD 20815
(301) 652-9495

*Hours:* 9:00 a.m.–5:00 p.m., Monday–Friday
*Person to Contact:* Charles Simpkinson, Ph.D, Director
*Founder:* Charles Simpkinson (1980)
*Owner:* Nonprofit educational organization
*Purpose:* Training and healing for psychotherapists and counselors
  seeking to integrate their spirituality into their professional and per-
  sonal life.
*Facilities:* Rented area retreat or training centers.
*Services:* Retreats, workshops, conferences, "kindred spirits network,"
  discussion groups for therapists interested in spirituality, through-
  out the entire United States.
*Visions and Goals:* Integration of spirituality and psychotherapy.
*Materials Available:* We publish a magazine and offer relevant books
  and tapes at a discount to subscribers.

# Lotus Yoga Center

1131 University Boulevard W., Room 1012, Silver Spring, MD 20902
(301) 649-4581

*Hours:* 9:30 a.m.–9:45 p.m., Monday–Thursday; 9:30 a.m.–4:30 p.m.,
  Saturday
*Person to Contact:* Riki Middleton, Director
*Founder/Owner:* Riki Middleton (May 1982)
*Purpose:* To help people realize their highest potential in body, mind
  and spirit through the art and science of yoga.
*Facilities:* Yoga studio and library.
*Services:* Classes in yoga exercises, breathing and relaxation, special
  classes in nutrition and meditation, lectures and seminars on a vari-
  ety of natural healing topics, Ayurvedic consultations, yoga for the
  disabled, and yoga retreats.
*Visions and Goals:* To specialize the yoga classes to fit particular
  "body types," according to the ancient Ayurvedic/Yoga health system. To nurture a greater understanding of "mother nature," our
  friends in the animal and plant world, through yoga.
*Materials Available:* Books and tapes and Ayurvedic health items.
  Library of yoga and health books.

# The Sunflower Yoga Company

1305 Chalmers Road, Silver Spring, MD 20903
(301) 445-3882

*Hours:* 6:00 a.m.–10:00 p.m., Monday–Friday; 10:00 a.m.–10:00 p.m.,
Saturday
*Person to Contact:* Sarabess or Wendy, Co-directors
*Founder/Owner:* Sarabess Forster and Wendy Zeroth (1980)
*Purpose:* For all the family to exercise, energize, relax, and rejuvenate.
*Facilities:* Yoga studio.
*Services:* Classes, workshops in yoga, meditation, stress management,
vegetarian cooking, rational fasting, and beach and mountain
retreats.
*Visions and Goals:* Peace begins within. A peaceful body creates a
peaceful mind, which reflects the expression of our spirit. We are all
searching for that spirit-nature or love. It is the reason for our existence. We have chosen the path of yoga instruction to assist others in
starting to discipline body and mind and as a means to our own
attainment of this peace and love.
*Materials Available:* Books, tapes, and posters.

# Under the Stars

S-30 Route 17 N., Paramus, NJ 07652
(201) 843-4455

*Hours:* 10:00 a.m.–7:00 p.m., Monday–Wednesday; 10:00 a.m.–9:00
p.m., Thursday and Friday; 10:00 a.m.–6:00 p.m., Saturday
*Person to Contact:* Sharon Lee Tesaurd, President
*Founder/Owner:* Sharon Lee Tesaurd (May 1987)
*Purpose:* A center for personal growth. Under the Stars is truly a com-
plete center with a staff that is knowledgeable, caring, and dedicated
to service.
*Facilities:* Retail/workshop space of 1,200 square ft. Parking for 100.
*Services:* Ongoing workshops and lectures with networking corner.
*Visions and Goals:* To provide information and products for alternative
healing and spiritual and educational development. We are quickly
moving toward owning a 9,000-square-foot facility where we will
have a full-time staff of holistic practitioners, and books, crystals,
New Age music, subliminal tapes, visionary art, videotape rental
department, and spiritual products for meditation and yoga.
*Materials Available:* Largest selection of holistic/personal growth
books, tapes, and music in New Jersey.

# Heights Holistic Health Associates

100 Remsen Street, Brooklyn, NY 11201
(718) 625-4802

*Hours:* 6 days a week by appointment
*Person to Contact:* Niravi B. Payne, Director
*Founder/Owner:* Niravi B. Payne, M.S. (1979)
*Purpose:* Programs and training courses which provide quality holistic
health care for individuals seeking natural healing methods or
adjunctive services to traditional medical practices. A Board-
certified internist and a psychotherapist offer unique holistic health
care services that truly address mind and body in the healing
process.
*Services:* Biofeedback, psychotherapy, and comprehensive medical and
nutritional services for a wide range of stress-related disorders,
ulcers, cancer, AIDS, ARC, and HIV positives.
*Visions and Goals:* The association is dedicated to helping individuals
discover that total emotional and physical health and healing is possible only when all systems of one's being ( mind, body, emotions,
and spirit ) are addressed in the process of heightened awareness of
well-being in total health, and illness, injury, and disease are seen as
opportunities for healing and growth.

# Wholistic Health Center

50 Maple Place, Manhasset, NY 11030
(516) 627-0309

*Hours:* 9:00 a.m.–7:30 p.m., Monday–Friday
*Person to Contact:* Faye Schenkman
*Founder:* Dr. and Mrs. Robert Sohn (1976)
*Owner:* Nonprofit organization
*Purpose:* To provide wholistic natural health care.
*Facilities:* Share the premises with a school, the New Center for
Wholistic Health Education and Research, and a health food store.
*Services:* Acupuncture, Amma therapy, biofeedback, counseling,
nutritional counseling, and chiropractic. We also offer a very suc-
cessful stop smoking acupuncture treatment.
*Visions and Goals:* A wholistic hospital.

# New Age Health Spa

Route 55, Neversink, NY 12765
(914) 985-7601

*Hours:* 7:30 a.m.–9:30 p.m., 7 days a week
*Person to Contact:* Werner Mendel, President
*Founder:* Elza Grayden (1965)
*Owner:* Werner Mendel
*Purpose:* A retreat for your mind, body and soul. To help people de-stress, detoxify, and discover their own loving, healthy, and happy self hiding inside. The New Age Health Spa seeks to be woven into each guest's life as a retreat where, over time, healthy eating habits and joyful exercise can be reinforced and developed. The New Age Health Spa offers itself as an active partner in each guest's quest to be happy, healthy, and wise.
*Facilities:* Situated on 155 acres of beautiful woods and meadows, the grounds, containing magnificent trees and wildflowers as well as hiking and cross-country skiing trails, contribute to feelings of serenity and peace. Thirty-nine rooms for lodging, indoor/outdoor pools, exercise room, store, video library, steam and sauna facilities, greenhouse and garden, beauty salon, and dining room that seats 90.
*Services:* We offer fitness programs, stretching, low-impact aerobic, aquatic, and toning classes, instruction in nautilus and weight equipment, and snowshoe or cross-country skiing. Consultations and classes with the staff nutrition and fitness counselors, also an extensive evening program of guest lecturers. T'ai Chi, meditation and yoga, Swedish massage, shiatsu, foot reflexology, loofa rubs, and Dead Sea mud treatments, aromatherapy sessions, facials, colonic irrigation, Ericksonian hypnosis, herbs and herbology, and work-shops. Delicious high-energy meals served.
*Visions and Goals:* To make a "Club Med" operation out of health retreats and spas—50 of them in various cities, affordable to the many.
*Miscellaneous:* Release of tension and stress has become increasingly important to each of us as is the opportunity to nurture body, mind, and soul. Exercise, yoga, massage, and a sensible meal management pattern are some of the techniques we emphasize to meet challenges.

When properly applied—and we teach you how—these activities can enhance self-appreciation and quality of life. At the New Age Health Spa, we have worked with nature to create an environment where you, like so many others, can achieve self-renewal and inner peace in a brief time.

The New Age Health Spa Credo:
We believe
—in giving people an opportunity to experience a wholesome environment that includes nutritious food, a comprehensive exercise program, resource persons and a well-stocked library.
—a supportive, wholesome environment encourages vitality and healthy self-concept.
—one can achieve and maintain ideal weight by eating nutritious foods.
—aerobic exercise significantly improves health, helps in sustaining ideal weight, increases self-esteem through fun, discipline, and mastery, and makes one feel and look good.
—knowledge is power and is vital to the ongoing development of beliefs, attitudes, and behaviors.
—a healthy spirit is a reflection of a curious mind and a well-cared-for body and a curious mind and well-cared-for body are reflections of healthy spirit.
—pleasure and play are keys that open the door to productivity, challenge, effort, and work.
—a support network of people who trust in common sense, intuition, and the innate ability to discover patterns of healthy living can help others reach their highest potential.

# Camp Lenox for Adults

345 Riverside Drive, #4C, New York, NY 10025
(212) 662-3182
Summer address: Route 8, Lee, MA 01238
(413) 243-2223

*Person to Contact:* Richard Moss, Director
*Founder:* Sperling family (1918)
*Owner:* Moss family since 1964
*Purpose:* While today's world is one of accelerated change and increasing complexity, a deep-rooted need still remains for the timeless values that nurture human spirit. Love, creativity, community, and a sense of the miraculous have been and continue to be guiding forces for a purposeful and well-lived life. Camp Lenox contributes to this rootedness in a way few experiences do. Our mountain retreat helps clear dust from the soul, while the programs celebrate the "spirit of life" and unity among people. You may come to Lenox for many reasons. For some, it's a time to reflect and deepen one's spiritual life; for others, it's a time for sport and recreation. Some come to Lenox to develop professional contacts, while others come to rediscover camp life and its childlike vitality.
*Facilities:* Camp Lenox sits on a hillside overlooking Shaw Lake in the Berkshire Mountains situated 1,700 feet above sea level on 250 acres of land. Housing includes 22 group cabins, 4 large community houses, 8 two-person cabins, and a tenting area for 150. Meeting facilities include indoor lodge used for seminars, dances, workshops or movies; 3 smaller meeting rooms, each able to accommodate 25 people; lakefront dining room, which seats 275; crafts center; and outdoor campfire amphitheater. Recreational facilities include 10 tennis courts, 10-acre athletic field, 3 basketball courts, and weight training room. Waterfront activities are sailing, swimming, windsurfing, canoeing, and kayaking.
*Services:* Programs such as "Northeast Medicine Wheel" with Sun Bear and "Sacred Psychology Seminar" with Jean Houston. Camp Lenox for Children, an eight-week residential program in sports, art, and community living for children ages 7-16. Also various conferences, workshops, and seminars. Gourmet vegetarian meals served. The camp is available for group rentals, ideal for large retreats and conferences, able to accommodate from 75 to 375 people. Our staff helps create the support system, food plan, and general tone most suited for your group needs.
*Visions and Goals:* We invite you to join us and contribute to the growing vision of peace and world renewal.

# New York Open Center, Inc.

83 Spring Street, New York, NY 10012
(212) 219-2527

*Hours:* 10:00 a.m.–10:00 p.m., 7 days a week

*Founder:* Walter Beebe (January 1984)

*Owner:* Nonprofit organization, member owned

*Purpose:* A holistic learning center with an avant-garde approach that could be described as a willingness to look for insight in places that few either dare or think to look. It is in part the ability to look back to find what has been forgotten; in part a leap into the unknown compelled by the urge to participate in creating tomorrow's mainstream. It is a willingness to abandon what is expected and look inside for what might be born. Should the avant-garde be exclusive to the arts? Where do we find the kinds of thought that would provide the same challenge and vitality in fields such as healing arts, psychology, philosophy, and science? In essence, our program explores these questions searching for emerging ideas and that gray area where ancient and modern understanding begin to blend in new ways. The Open Center presents individuals whose work offers an "inside" look into world culture's deepest interests.

*Facilities:* First 3 stories of Soho Building, six classroom/performance spaces, small bookstore, meditation room.

*Services:* Ongoing classes, workshops, lectures, and performances. Nine hundred events a year provide instruction covering both traditional practice and the most advanced medical research in such topics as Laying-on-of-Hands; African, Native American, Western, and Oriental Shamanistic Healing; Tibetan, Christian, and Kabalistic Meditation; wholistic approaches to depression, addictions, cancer, and AIDS; herbology; Feldenkrais; shiatsu; acupressure; and T'ai Chi. Instructors are Bernard Siegel, M.D.; Andrew Weil, M.D.; Dr. Yeshi Donden; Dolores Krieger, Ph.D., R.N.; Don Juan Camargo; Rosalyn Bruyere-Zuspan; Ted Kapchuk, M.D.; Red Thunder Cloud; Sam Keen, Ph.D.; James Bugenthal, Ph.D.; Stanley Krippner, Ph.D.; Marion Woodman; and Stephen Chang, M.D., among others.

*Visions and Goals:* Our goal is to bring fresh and life-enhancing concepts, which may be entirely original or reemerging from ancient traditions, into the fabric of everyday life.

*Materials Available:* Quality books dealing with the holistic, spiritual, social, and ecological dimensions of individual and cultural transformation. Also music and workshop tapes, calendars, cards, and jewelry.

# Creative Aging, Inc.

700 West End Avenue, 11B, New York, NY 10025
(212) 864-1523

*Hours:* 9:00 a.m.–5:00 p.m., Monday–Friday
*Person to Contact:* Johanna Vandenberg, Executive Director
*Founder/Owner:* Johanna Vandenberg (January 1981)
*Purpose:* To transform the quality and image of aging into growth and
   fulfillment. Creative Aging, Inc. is committed to a wellness perspective in which the human imagination is allowed free rein in exploring the possibilities and implications of self-empowerment and
   aging. We incorporate the full range of human technology, a neces-
   sary move away from limitation and fear of aging and disease.
*Facilities:* Central office.
*Services:* Ongoing lectures, programs, written materials. Introduction
   to concepts and methods designed to master the aging process.
*Visions and Goals:* To reverse the disease model of aging—the victimi-
   zation.

# New Age Center

One South Broadway, Nyack, NY 10960
(914) 353-2590

*Hours:* 8:00 a.m.–11:00 p.m., 7 days a week
*Person to Contact:* Kenneth Pollinger, Director
*Founder/Owner:* Kenneth Pollinger, Ph. D. (January 1983)
*Purpose:* We are interested in integration and transformation, through
   awareness of body, mind, emotions and spirit. We are primarily a
   healing/spiritual center. We want to assist individuals in changing
   their old patterns of thinking, feeling, and acting to a more wholistic
   way of being.
*Facilities:* A 3-story building in the heart of downtown Nyack, a
   health food market, and a deli.
*Services:* Weekly Zen, yogic and kabalistic meditation; over 30 yoga
   classes per week at different levels, Tai Chi, Aikido, dance, aerobics,
   training in ohashiatsu, massage, and over 50 New Age workshops
   per semester.
*Materials Available:* Books, tapes, crystals, music, and yoga supplies
   sold at the Health Food Market.

# Omega Institute for Holistic Studies

Lake Drive, RD 2, Box 377, Rhinebeck, NY 12572
September 15–May 15 (914) 338-6030; May 15–September 15 (414) 266-4301

*Hours:* 10:00 a.m.–5:00 p.m., Monday–Friday
*Person to Contact:* Sarah Priestman, Administrative Director
*Founder:* Stefan Rechtschaffen and Elizabeth Lesser (1977)
*Owner:* Nonprofit corporation
*Purpose:* A learning retreat and conference center; a community for participants and summer staff and a vacation environment, encouraging study, creativity, play, and a relationship to the great outdoors.
*Facilities:* Omega's 80-acre lakefront campus is located on gentle rolling hills in the beautiful Hudson Valley. Participants stay in private or shared cottage rooms, dorms, or their own tents. Dining hall, classrooms, sauna, Omega Cafe, Omega Massage Center with flotation tank, the Tape Shop, the Omega Bookstore, and the Mountain Gem Crafts Shop.
*Services:* Two hundred weekend and weeklong workshops, during the three-month summer season. Workshops at Omega explore new ideas in the arts, psychology, health, fitness, business, global thinking, spirituality, and preventative medicine. The distinguished faculty are leaders and innovators in their fields. A past and present sampling include: R. D. Laing, Elizabeth Kübler-Ross, noted psychiatrists; Ashley Montagu, Joseph Chilton Pearce, authors; Fritjof Capra, Edgar Mitchell, scientists, futurists; Robert Bly, Gary Snyder, Allen Ginsberg, Anne Waldman, poets; Pete Seeger, Bobby McGerrin, Max Roach, Odetta, musicians; Christopher Alexander, Keith Critchlow, architects. Fees include meals (primarily vegetarian and creatively prepared to provide excellent nutrition), evening concerts, dances, optional daily classes in yoga, meditation, T'ai Chi and aerobics, sauna, swimming, and boating. We also sponsor educational and wilderness trips throughout the world, four weeks of winter programs on St. John's Island in the U.S. Virgin Islands, and winter courses at other sites in the Northeast.
*Visions and Goals:* To initiate the Service Education and Retreat Center, which is envisioned as an ongoing extensive training and retreat center for those in the service field.
*Materials Available:* Audiotapes of current and past Omega workshops, a wide selection of books, an unusual collection of jewelry, clothing, musical instruments, and artifacts from around the world.

# Foundation for "A Course in Miracles" Conference/Retreat Center

RD 2, Box 71, Roscoe, NY 12776
(607) 498-4116

*Hours:* 9:00 a.m.–5:00 p.m., Monday–Friday
*Person to Contact:* Judy Beck
*Founder:* Kenneth and Gloria Wapnick (January 1983)
*Owner:* Nonprofit corporation
*Purpose:* To foster spiritual development through the study and practice of A Course in Miracles (ACIM).
*Facilities:* Located on 95 acres in the Catskill Mountains. The property includes comfortable accommodations for up to 90 people. Plus 25 acres of beautiful Tennanah Lake, suitable for swimming, boating, fishing, and ice skating in the winter. Tennis court, indoor swimming pool, sauna, and walking trails.
*Services:* Weeklong and weekend seminars, workshops, and small classes, all covering ACIM.
*Visions and Goals:* To provide a setting where people can learn ACIM and integrate it into their lives.
*Materials Available:* Books and tapes.

# Wainwright House

260 Stuyvesant Avenue, Rye, NY 10580
(914) 967-6080

*Hours:* 9:00 a.m.–5:00 p.m., 7 days a week
*Person to Contact:* Receptionist
*Founded:* 1941
*Owner:* Nonprofit/nonsectarian
*Purpose:* To provide support for those in search of intellectual, pychological, physical, and spiritual growth.
*Facilities:* Located in a stately stone mansion on five acres overlooking Long Island Sound. Overnight accommodations, meals served, bookstore and library.
*Services:* Courses, workshops, and seminars offered year-round, with leaders such as Ram Dass, David Spangler and Barbara Marx Hubbard. There are four institutes: Health and Healing, Depth Psychology, Global Issues, and Spiritual Development.
*Visions and Goals:* Over the years, the concern for the whole individual and the whole earth has been the driving motivation of the Wainwright House mission.
*Materials Available:* Books.

# Sharon Springs Health Spa

Box 288-A Chestnut Street, Sharon Springs, NY 13459
(518) 284-2885

*Hours:* 7 days a week
*Person to Contact:* Delores Schneider, Director
*Founder/Owner:* Delores Schneider (1982)
*Purpose:* To rejuvenate, regenerate and revitalize naturally. Sharon Springs is famous for its health-giving mineral spring waters and therapeutic sulphur baths. Whether you are desirous of slenderizing, toning up your body, detoxification, educational stimulus, or just a "change of pace" vacation, you will be counseled individually and the optimum program will be selected for you.
*Facilities:* Sauna, jacuzzi, exercise equipment, mineral springs nearby.
*Services:* Holistic-oriented workshops, nutritional program, exercise program, educational programs. Options include massage, iridology, hydrotherapy, reflexology, herbal wraps, mud baths, facials, sulphur baths, Reiki, private counseling, nutrition, and diet.

# Wise Woman Center

P.O. Box 64, Woodstock, NY 12498
(914) 246-8081

*Hours:* 24 hours a day, 7 days a week, March–November
*Person to Contact:* Susun Weed, Director
*Founder/Owner:* Susun Weed (1979)
*Purpose:* The Wise Woman Center is a safe space for self-healing and a
   delightful class setting filled with capricious goats, funny fairies,
   and wild weeds. It exists to reweave the Wise Woman Way.
*Facilities:* Fifty acres of densely wooded Catskill Mountain beauty.
   Large swimming pond with sunning deck, private river swimming
   and public swimming in the cascades, gardens, meeting lodge tipi,
   moon lodge tipi, dorm and campsite accommodations, and fabulous
   vegetarian meals.
*Services:* Self-healing retreats, workshops, intensives, and apprenticeships in wise woman herbal medicine, spirit healing skills, and
   green witchcraft.
*Visions and Goals:* The wise woman tradition focuses on healing ourselves and the earth holographically, wholly through optimum
   nourishment, simple ritual, and peaceful compassion. The goal of
   the center is to make this tradition known and accessible.

# Prana (Philadelphia Resource and Networking Association)

Center for Holistic Education and Self-Development
638 South Street, Philadelphia, PA 19147
(215) 592-9035

*Hours:* 24 hours a day, 7 days a week
*Person to Contact:* Ruth Hoskins, President/Director
*Founder/Owner:* Ruth Hoskins (1984)
*Purpose:* Holistic education, a teaching center and spiritual retreat, networking.
*Facilities:* Magnificent office space at 638 South Street.
*Services:* Workshops in massage and the I Am Spiritual Group. Ongoing groups, such as yoga. Other workshops include past-life regression, ascended master teachings, astrology, and a sensuality playshop. Retreats are offered 2 to 3 times a year in the Philadelphia/NJ/NY area. Massage including deep muscle, Trager, Swedish, sensate touch, reflexology, Reiki, deep tissue, shiatsu, spinology.
*Visions and Goals:* Continued holistic education.
*Materials Available:* Bimonthly newsletter, Connexions. Mail order service of tapes, books, crystals, and health-related products.

# Foundation for Well-Being

P.O. Box 627, Plymouth Meeting, PA 19462
(215) 828-4674

*Hours:*. 9:00 a.m.–6:00 p.m., Monday–Friday
*Person to Contact:* Philip H. Friedman, Ph.D., Executive Director
*Founder/Owner:* Philip Friedman (January 1976)

*Purpose:* To enhance psychological, emotional, relational, physical, and spiritual well-being and to experience and share love.
*Facilities:* Two offices, one in Plymouth Meeting and one in Philadelphia.
*Services:* Seminars, workshops, courses, intensives, psychotherapy, and assessment guidance.
*Visions and Goals:* To promote healing, joy, harmony, peace, forgiveness, and well-being in individuals, couples, families, groups, institutions, countries, and the world.
*Materials Available:* Articles, tapes, and a book in process.

# The Himalayan Institute

RR 1, Box 400, Honesdale, PA 18431
(717) 253-5551

*Hours:* 9:00 a.m.–5:00 p.m., Monday–Saturday
*Person to Contact:* Katherine Avlonitis or Dale Colton, Public
  Relations
*Founder:* Swami Rama (1971)
*Owner:* Nonprofit organization
*Purpose:* The Himalayan Institute is dedicated to teaching the various
  aspects of yoga and meditation as a means to foster the personal
  growth of the individual and the betterment of society. The goals of
  the institute are achieved through numerous educational, therapeutic, and research programs. These innovative programs provide a
  highly respected and reliable source of information and practical
  training to those interested in self-directed change.
*Facilities:* The 422-acre campus is nestled in the rolling hills of the
  Pocono Mountains. Surrounded by spectacular views of wooded hills
  and valleys are the various educational, therapeutic, research, publishing, and residential facilities of the institute. Approximately 190
  residents and guests can be accommodated in over 100 double-
  occupancy rooms in the main building, which also houses classrooms, offices, medical facilities, an auditorium, library, woodwork-
  ing shop, homeopathic pharmacy, and India Imports gift shop. Facilities also include the Himalayan Publishers press building,
  warehouse, and the Eleanor N. Dana Research Laboratory, the Children's Center, which includes a modern playground and school,
  organic vegetable gardens, orchard, apiary and greenhouse, hiking
  trails, small lake ideal for swimming and ice skating, and abundant
  countryside for cross-country skiing. There are recreational facilities for tennis, volleyball, and other outdoor sports.
*Services:* Yoga classes, weekend seminars on over 50 topics from
  biofeedback and the science of breath to natural health care and the
  positive use of emotions. The institute offers a variety of options for
  personal growth and development, and professional-level training
  courses. Vegetarian meals are served.
*Visions and Goals:* "By being aware of one's own potential and abilities, one can become a perfect citizen, help the nation, and serve
  humanity." (Swami Rama)
*Materials Available:* In addition to printing and distributing over fifty
  books, the Institute also publishes three periodicals: The
  *Himalayan News, Dawn* magazine, and the *Research Bulletin.*

# Creative Energy Options

909 Sumneytown Pike, Box 603, Springhouse, PA 19477
(215) 643-4420

*Hours:* 9:00 a.m.–5:00 p.m., Monday–Friday, for therapy
*Person to Contact:* Sylvia Lafair, Director
*Founder/Owner:* Sylvia Lafair and Herb Kaufman (1985)
*Purpose:* To provide a forum for self-discovery using many paths to
that deep inner knowing we all experience.
*Facilities:* Suite of offices in Springhouse, including classrooms, work-
rooms, therapy rooms and bookstore/gift store. Retreat center in
White Haven, Pennsylvania (Poconos).
*Services:* Personal growth groups from pregnancy through the golden
years. Workshops, classes, special events, programs, and seminars.
Individual psychotherapy, childbirth classes, Reiki/polarity treat-
ments, and massage.
*Visions and Goals:* To continue our dream of creating a safe space for
people to grow, to move from knowledge to understanding, from
understanding to wisdom.
*Materials Available:* Books and tapes.

# American Institute of Metaphysics (AIMS)

2000 L Street N.W., Suite #200, Washington, D.C. 20036
(202) 659-0689

*Hours:* 8:30 a.m.–5:30 p.m,. Monday–Friday
*Person to Contact:* Lonnie Wornom
*Founder/Owner:* Dianne Lancaster (1981)
*Purpose:* To establish a multidisciplinary holistic training designed to
teach and certify practitioners as metaphysicians. The AIMS program teaches the principles and methods of merging ego and soul
consciousness, enabling the individual to develop intuitive guidance from the soul.
*Facilities:* Office in Washington, D.C., and a staff house in Vienna, Virginia. (703) 938-8812.
*Services:* Metaphysicians certification program, individual counseling, intuitive business analysis, Atlantean numerology and tarot,
classes and correspondence courses in soul- and self-development.
*Visions and Goals:* To offer to the general public an introduction to the
principles of metaphysics and an understanding of how the universe
works. Also to offer to practitioners a program that prepares them to
be loving, confident, intuitive counselors and therapists.
*Materials Available:* Correspondence courses.

## Holistic Health Clinic

5605 16th Street, N.W., Washington, D.C. 20011
(202) 723-4510

*Hours:* 10:00 a.m.–5:00 p.m., Monday–Saturday
*Person to Contact:* Dr. P. Spero Tsindos, Director
*Founder:* Rev. Henry Nagorka
*Purpose:* To help individuals heal themselves, drawing on a number of different modalities.
*Services:* Homeopathy, nutrition, counseling, herbalism, massage, and summer workshops.
*Visions and Goals:* To ensure the continued health of all those who attend us. *Mens sana in corpore sano.*
*Miscellaneous:* There are certain fundamentals of holistic healing which are as follows: Healing is a principle of Nature. This principle should be invoked by natural means. The whole person should be the focus, not the disease alone. Ill-health is due to either ignorance of or flouting of Nature's laws of health and well-being. Ill-health is not a personal problem alone but multifactorial and sociological. The main therapy is educational. The holistic treatment of minor problems prevents major problems from occurring. The individual should be deeply involved in the healing process.

## Sri Chinmoy Centre

3502 Connecticut Avenue N.W., Washington, D.C. 20008
(202) 363-4797

*Hours:* 9:00 a.m.–5:00 p.m., Monday–Friday
*Person to Contact:* Kalika Novoa, President
*Founder:* Sri Chinmoy
*Purpose:* A meditation path to lead people to God-realization and love of God through the opening of the heart.
*Facilities:* Meditation center, gift and card shop, school for children ages 4-12, based on peace and the philosophy of Sri Chinmoy.
*Services:* Free weekly classes in meditation, peace concerts (music for meditation), and weekly meditations at the U.S. Congress. Monthly running races. Annual spiritual poetry awards and an annual spiritual arts festival.
*Materials Available:* Books and tapes by Sri Chinmoy.

## More Centers/Retreats

### Connecticut

*Horizons (at the Ecos Center)*    Box 331, Farmington, CT 06032
(203-677-1588)
*Integral Health Services*    245 School Street, Putnam, CT 06260
(203-928-7729)
*Friends of EKR*    123B Wolcott Hill Road, Welhersfield, CT 06109
(203-563-3035)
*Rivendell Holistic Retreat*    3 Old Mill Road, Weston, CT 06883
(203-227-3559)

### Maryland

*New Life Clinic*    1301 Ashbury Road, Baltimore, MD 21209
(301-435-9736)
*Moonridge*    4344 Aitcheson Road, Beltsville, MD 20705
(301-470-3033)
*The Centering Institute*    6109 Broad Street, Bethesda, MD 20816
(301-229-8890)
*Transpersonal Institute*    4933 Auburn Avenue, Bethesda, MD 20814
*Claggett Retreat Center*    3035 Buckeystown Pike, Buckeystown, MD
21717 (301-874-5147)
*Network of Light*    4617 Hunt Avenue, Chevy Chase, MD 20815
(301-986-1223)
*Studies of Human Systems Center*    8604 Jones Mill Road, Chevy
Chase, MD 20015 (301-657-8299)
*Pyramid Foundation*    P.O. Box 3759, Frederick, MD 21701
(301-694-9761)
*The Rotunda Center for Attitudinal Healing*    15 Kitzbuhel, Parton,
MD 21120 (301-467-6333)
*Rockville Health Association*    4808 Macon Road, Rockville, MD
20852 (301-881-2406)

### New Jersey

*Harbor Island Spa*    701 Ocean Avenue, West End, Long Branch, NJ
07746 (201-222-5800)
*The Healing Heart Center*    189 George Street, New Brunswick, NJ
08901 (201-247-3723)

*Princeton Area Holistic Health*   360 Nassau Street, Princeton, NJ 08540 (609-924-8580)

## New York

*Friends of EKR*   790 Lancaster Street, Albany, NY 12203 (518-489-4431)

*Friends of EKR*   1877 E. 12th Street, Brooklyn, NY 11229 (718-375-5288)

*Friends of EKR*   315 6th Avenue, Brooklyn, NY 11215 (718-768-7953)

*The Moving Center*   Box 712, Cooper Station, NY 10276 (212-505-7928)

*Taoist Esoteric Yoga Center*   Box 1194, Huntington, NY 11743 (516-549-9452)

*Pawling Health Manor*   Box 401, Hyde Park, NY 12538 (914-887-4141)

*Foundation of Light*   399 Turkey Hill Road, Ithaca, NY 14850

*Roots and Wings*   153-7 Zena Highwoods Road, Kingston, NY 12401 (914-679-5580)

*Friends of EKR*   6 Russet Lane, Lake Grove, NY 11755 (516-467-6582)

*Attitudinal Healing Center of Long Island*   1691 Northern Boulevard, Manhasset, NY 11030 (516-625-0770)

*Aegis-The Adobe*   RD 1, Box 10301, New Lebanon, NY 12125 (518-794-8095)

*Circle of Light Institute*   505 8th Avenue, #219, New York, NY 10018 (212-564-2477)

*Friends of EKR*   61 Hitchcock Lane, Old Westbury, NY 11568 (516-997-9713)

*Awosting Retreat*   Box 367, Parksville, NY 12768

*Phoenicia Pathwork Center*   Box 66, Phoenicia, NY 12464 (914-688-2211)

*Wholistic Health Education Center*   715 Monroe Avenue, Rochester, NY 14607 (716-442-5480)

*Center for Attitudinal Healing*   P.O. Box 111, Roslyn Heights, NY 11577

*Fannie Shaffer's Hotel*   Box 457, Woodridge, NY 12789 (914-434-4455)

## Pennsylvania

*The Renaissance Group*   36A Bridge Street, Doylestown, PA 18901 (215-340-1532)

*Aquarian Research Foundation*   5620 Morton Street, Philadelphia, PA 19144 (215-849-1259)

*Philadelphia Well-Being Center*   2475 S. Napfle Street, Philadelphia, PA 19152 (215-332-6996)

*Genesis Center*    68 N. 2nd Street, Philadelphia, PA 19382
(215-928-1323)
*Kripalu Yoga Ashram*    7 Waters Road, Box 250, Sumneytown, PA
18084 (215-234-4568)
*Re-Vitalization Centers*    Box 313, Upper Darby, PA 19082
(215-352-7017)
*The Living Awareness Foundation*    P.O. Box 343, Wallingford, PA
19086 (215-565-5819)

**Washington, D.C.**
*3HO Center for Holistic Living*    1704 Q Street N.W., Washington,
D.C. 20009 (202-435-5599)
*Cedar Hill Retreat*    6926 Willow Street N.W., Washington, D.C.
20012 (202-829-3289)
*Center for Attitudinal Healing*    4530 16th Street N.W., Washington,
D.C. 20016 (202-797-5522)
*Georgetown Healing Arts Center*    1015 Wisconsin Avenue N.W.,
Washington, D.C. 20007 (202-337-0347)
*Natural Health Clinic*    1455 Harvard Street N.W., Washington, D.C.
20009 (202-667-5162)
*Potomac Massage Therapy Institute*    421 Butternut Street N.W.,
Washington, D.C. 20012 (202-829-4201)
*Synergy*    4321 Wisconsin Avenue N.W., Washington, D.C. 20016
(202-363-4664)
*The Institute Center*    3413 Wisconsin Avenue N.W., Washington,
D.C. 20016 (202-362-2456)

# Part X: The Southeast

# Shangri-La Health Resort

P.O. Box 2328, Bonita Springs, FL 33959
(813) 992-3811

*Hours:* 8:00 a.m.–9:00 p.m., 7 days a week
*Person to Contact:* John Cheatham
*Founder:* R.J. Cheatham (1964)
*Owner:* Frances E. Cheatham
*Purpose:* To teach the concepts of healthy living.
*Facilities:* Hotel-motel accommodations available, vegetarian meals, pool, solariums, tennis courts, health food, and bookstore.
*Services:* Lectures and classes in all phases of natural hygiene: food combining, food preparation, sprouting, fasting, permanent weight loss, mental and emotional poise, meditation and relaxation, self-awareness, movements rhythmics, yoga, chair-exercises, toning, firming, and recontouring, pool exercises, organic gardening, stress management, and private consultations. A wide variety of recreational activities, including beach trips.
*Materials Available:* Health food and books.


# Hunuman Foundation Library

P.O. Box 2320, Delray Beach, FL 33447
(407) 272-9165

*Hours:* 9:00 a.m.–5:00 p.m., Monday–Saturday
*Person to Contact:* Bob Zaslow, Manager
*Founder:* Ram Dass (1973)
*Owner:* Nonprofit foundation
*Purpose:* To promote spiritual well-being through education and service, by spiritual training, publications, and video recordings.
*Facilities:* We have no center or physical institutional framework, but offer workshops and retreats nationally and abroad. We have a spiritual temple in Taos, which is known as the Hunuman Temple or Neem Karoli Baba Ashram. Its address is Drawer W, Taos, NM 87571.
*Services:* We have developed service projects, which now function independently, such as the Prison-Ashram Project and the Living/Dying Project. We also provide information on the speaking and retreat schedules of Ram Dass and Stephen Levine.
*Materials Available:* Books, audiotapes and videotapes are listed in our catalogs.

# Regency Health Resort & Spa

2000 S. Ocean Drive, Hallandale, FL 33009
(305) 454-2220

*Hours:* 10:00 a.m.–6:00 p.m., Monday–Friday
*Person to Contact:* Mort Pine, President
*Founder/Owner:* H. Gross and Mort Pine (1984)
*Purpose:* A national health learning center combining a program
   designed to teach life extension and enjoyment in a luxury class
   beach resort environment. A holistic, vegetarian resort.
*Facilities:* Fifty rooms on the oceanfront, gourmet vegetarian meals,
   heated pool, jacuzzi, sauna, and exercise equipment.
*Services:* Lectures and classes in all phases of health. Nutrition classes
   and counseling, supervised exercise programs (yoga, non-impact and
   regular aerobics, water exercises, exercise equipment, etc.), meditation and relaxation, stress reduction, behavior modification, smoking seminars, supervised juice- and water-fasting, skin care and
   make-up consultation, and massage. Vegetarian health and diet programs are medically supervised. Also evening programs of fun and
   entertainment.
*Visions and Goals:* To assist people to become healthy, positive, and
   vital.

# Aslan House, Jacksonville Center for Attitudinal Healing

P.O. Box 52116, Jacksonville, FL 32201
(904) 353-4357 (HELP)

*Hours:* 8:30 a.m.–5:00 p.m., Monday, Wednesday, Thursday, Friday;
   8:30 a.m.–9:00 p.m., Tuesday
*Person to Contact:* Paula Hinson, Director
*Founder:* Paula Hinson (October 1986)
*Purpose:* To enable individuals to let go of the emotional pain and fear
   that usually accompany a catastrophic illness or death of a loved one
   and begin to lead a more fulfilling and peaceful life.
*Facilities:* Office/meeting room—2nd floor classroom building at
   Riverside Park Methodist Church.
*Services:* First and third Tuesday, adult groups, patients, and families.
   Second and fourth Tuesday, children's groups, with families.
   Microtel "Phone Pal" network.
*Visions and Goals:* We plan to add daytime groups, sponsored outings,
   seminars for parents, and "Elders" program for senior citizens, and a
   Vietnam Vets group.
*Materials Available:* Lending library: books, audio- and videotapes.

# Russell House of Key West

611 Truman Avenue, Key West, FL 33040
(305) 294-8787

*Hours:* 24 hours a day, 7 days a week
*Person to Contact:* Sharon
*Founder/Owner:* Enid R. Badler (May 1979)
*Purpose:* Health-oriented programs for relaxation, cleansing, weight loss, and smoking elimination through diet and exercise.
*Facilities:* A European-style health resort in historic old Key West with 24 guest rooms, complete spa facilities, boutique, bookstore, pool, and tropical gardens.
*Services:* Weight loss, smoking elimination, life-style and nutrition classes, yoga, aquathenics, daily seminars, exercise program, and complete holistic program. Nutritional therapies used are holistic, natural vegetarian meals, and juice fasting. Massage and body work as well as complete beauty treatments are also available.
*Visions and Goals:* Our program has helped thousands of people nationwide change their lives through taking responsibility for their own selves. We seek slimmer, healthier, and happier people everywhere.

# Project Rainbow Consulting Services

7529 3rd Avenue North, St. Petersburg, FL 33710
(813) 345-2698

*Hours:* By appointment
*Person to Contact:* Barbara Hamilton
*Founder/Owner:* Barbara Hamilton (February 1987)
*Purpose:* To found centers to give emotional support to families of chronically ill children and provide training to related agencies. To provide private consultations fostering the development of one's divine potential and the unity of body, mind, and spirit.
*Services:* Consultations and training in replication of a model program, imagery and personal empowerment, death and dying, holistic healing, and personal transformation.
*Visions and Goals:* To create a network of centers that foster the higher purpose in each of us, particularly our children, thus creating a better world for all.
*Materials Available:* Brochures and tapes.

## The Life Center

214 S. Fielding Avenue, Tampa, FL 33606
(813) 251-0289

*Hours:* 10:00 a.m.–8:00 p.m., Monday–Friday
*Person to Contact:* Sheryle R. Baker, M.A.
*Founder:* Dr. Marilyn Gatlin and Dr. Martin D. Cohen (1981)
*Owner:* Nonprofit
*Purpose:* To provide emotional support to adults/children dealing with any life-threatening illness or death, free of charge.
*Services:* Free counseling and support groups; for example, rebuilding from loss, coping with illness, teen grief support, suicide loss. Stress workshops, employee assistance, and special topic seminars.
*Visions and Goals:* To obtain the funds to provide more educational and training programs for professionals in the fields of death and bereavement and for the services to be used by corporations' consultants.
*Miscellaneous:* The uniqueness of T.L.C. (learning to deal with inner feeling effectively) is that it is a grass-roots agency. It is supported by volunteers and many professionals (counselors, psychologists, etc.). We are supported by donations and corporate funding.

## The Atlanta Center for Attitudinal Awareness

P.O. Box 675015, Marietta, GA 30067
(404) 953-3136

*Hours:* 9:00 a.m.–5:00 p.m., Monday–Friday
*Person to Contact:* Patricia Zerman, Director
*Founder:* Patricia Zerman (May 1988)
*Owner:* Nonprofit organization
*Purpose:* To release the fears that block us from inner peace. We teach peace instead of conflict, love rather than fear. We are based in part on the Center for Attitudinal Healing in Tiburon, California, which was founded by Jerry Jampolsky, M.D. We also follow the writings of surgeon Bernie Siegel as well as Louise Hay.
*Facilities:* Offices and classrooms.
*Services:* Support groups, classes, and workshops.
*Visions and Goals:* To offer more classes on personal growth and awareness and continuing growth with support and services.

# United Research Light Center

2200 Highway 9, South (P.O. Box 1146), Black Mountain, NC 28711
(704) 669-6845

*Hours:* 9:00 a.m.–9:00 p.m., Monday–Friday; open 24 hours a day for
prayer.
*Founder:* James V. Goure (1970)
*Owner:* Nonprofit corporation
*Purpose:* The accomplishment of 24-hour prayer for Planet Earth and
providing techniques for spiritual transformation based on divine
light and love.
*Facilities:* The two-story geodesic dome features beautiful prayer and
meditation rooms, an audiovisual library and bookstore on 181 acres
of woods, a mountain stream, walking trails, and meditation gardens
in the Pisgah Mountain range.
*Services:* Regular group prayer for personal and planetary healing;
weekly classes and lectures; prayer weekends; one-, two-, and three-
day workshops, intensives and advances focusing on techniques on
transformation in an environment of high spiritual energy; "Healing
of the Nations" trips to accomplish round-the-clock prayer in the
capital cities of the world.

# Cheerhope, Inc.

29 Davis Branch Road, Bryson City, NC 28713
(704) 488-6920

*Hours:* 24 hours a day, 7 days a week
*Person to Contact:* Rose Morningstar, President
*Founder:* Rose Morningstar (1984)
*Owner:* Nonprofit organization
*Purpose:* To provide a place for self-healing for those who are in emotional distress, to encourage independence and wholeness of
thought about oneself and one's ability to enjoy life, to help people
learn to choose wisely in structuring their own environment and
their life-force, to build a center that improves upon those currently
dedicated to emotional healing, and to show the way by allowing
those who work their way to health to enlighten us all about human
love and caring.
*Facilities:* A beautiful healing garden of 44 acres, vegetables, berries
and fruit trees, hiking trails through the woods, building with large
library.
*Services:* Counseling, Reiki, space for personal vision quests, physical
therapy, emotional healing, and gardening.
*Visions and Goals:* We have a vision, a lot of faith, and determination.

# Unity Center for Growth and Healing

3500 Sharon View Road, Charlotte, NC 28211
(704) 553-0756

*Hours:* 9:00 a.m.–5:00 p.m., Monday–Friday
*Person to Contact:* Jervais Phillips, Elizabeth Phillips, Ginny Wright, Robin Alstrin
*Founded:* June 1988
*Owner:* Sponsored by Unity of Charlotte
*Purpose:* Spiritual counseling and other modes of healing.
*Facilities:* Listening and meditation room and group room.
*Services:* Quiet space for meditation and listening to tapes; support group and spiritual counseling for individuals and couples.
*Visions and Goals:* We hope to have a residential program, a place where people in spiritual need can come and be supported.
*Materials Available:* Unity tapes, music tapes.

# Southern Dharma Retreat Center

Route 1, Box 34-H, Hot Springs, NC 28743
(704) 622-7112

*Hours:* 24 hours a day, 7 days a week
*Person to Contact:* Barbara Acker, Co-manager
*Founder:* Elizabeth Kent (December 1978)
*Owner:* A public, nonprofit educational organization
*Purpose:* To provide meditation retreats from a diversity of spiritual traditions and to provide a comfortable gathering place removed from the everyday hassles of life and to create an atmosphere of quiet calmness where one can nurture a sense of peace and uncover the truth within the heart.
*Facilities:* Remote, rural mountainous setting, a dormitory that sleeps 25, a meditation hall that sits 35, campsites, one retreat cabin, and a library (housed in the dorm).
*Services:* Teacher-led retreats, private, individual retreats, private and group retreats, and workshops. Vegetarian meals served.
*Visions and Goals:* To maintain the eclectic, independent, and non-denominational nature of the center.
*Materials Available:* Books and audio- and videotapes available in the library.

## The Quest Institute, Inc.

P.O. Box 3265, Charlottesville, VA 22903
(804) 295-6923

*Hours:* 10:00 a.m.–8:00 p.m., Monday–Friday; 10:00 a.m.–5:30 p.m.,
  Saturday
*Person to Contact:* Kay Allison
*Founder:* Kay Allison (1984)
*Owner:* Private, nonprofit, educational corporation
*Purpose:* To explore issues of human consciousness beyond the tradi-
  tional limits of academic study. To integrate science and spirituality
  in a comprehensive search for truth. To stimulate spiritual and
  holistic human development. To encourage exploration of the inner
  world. To encourage interreligious dialogue as a means to global har-
  mony and peace.
*Facilities:* Bookstore, espresso coffee corner, and other buildings.
*Services:* Organizes lectures, courses, conferences, and experiential
  workshops to achieve our objectives.
*Visions and Goals:* The institute came about as an outgrowth of the
  classes and workshops offered through the bookstore. A second
  bookstore is currently planned in northern Virginia.
*Materials Available:* Books, crystals, crystal jewelry, videos, tapes, etc.

## The Winged Heart Homestead
## (The Penny Royal Educational Center, Inc.)

P.O. Box 552, Floyd, VA 24091
(703) 763-3728

*Hours:* Before 7:00 a.m. or after 7:00 p.m.
*Person to Contact:* Muzawir
*Founder/Owner:* Muzawir (1978)
*Purpose:* To promote the building of the "Universel," a temple where
  all world religions will be united in one structure. To develop the
  farm.
*Facilities:* Two hundred eighty-three acres where camping facilities
  only are available at present.
*Services:* Training in yoga and sufism. A summer camp is planned for
  the summer of 1989 where emphasis will be given on sufism, yoga,
  and related subjects, such as how to use your psychic abilities,
  telepathy, and healing through meditative practices and how, practi-
  cally, to apply these methods in everyday life.
*Visions and Goals:* To build individual shelters for members as well as
  to utilize the farm.

## *Little Stony Creek Haven*
Route 1, Box 359-C, Edinburg, VA 22824
(703) 984-4462

*Hours:* Open 7 days a week
*Person to Contact:* Lee or Christine, Owners
*Founder/Owner:* Lee and Christine Jacobsen (March 1987)
*Purpose:* To offer a place to rest and bring balance back into your life.
   We are specially geared to provide a place for people who live in cit-
   ies to spend time in nature.
*Facilities:* One fully furnished guest cottage that can sleep up to 7. All
   you need bring is your own food.
*Services:* Guided meditations, Reiki, flower essence therapy plus
   plenty of space for those who need it.
*Visions and Goals:* To make the world a better place.
*Materials Available:* Metaphysical books, farm pond and canoe, a
   mountain creek with swimming area.
*Miscellaneous:* Our 35-acre farm adjoins the George Washington
   National Forest, providing unlimited trails for hiking. Our animals
   include friendly cats, rabbits, goats, and a dog.

# The Elisabeth Kübler-Ross Center (Shanti Nilaya)

South Route 616, Headwaters, VA 24442
(703) 396-3441

*Hours:* 9:00 a.m.–5:00 p.m., Monday–Friday

*Founder:* Elisabeth Kübler-Ross, M.D. (1977). Originally known as Shanti Nilaya, Sanskrit meaning "home of peace."

*Owner:* A nonprofit, nonsectarian organization dedicated to the enhancement of life and growth through the practice of unconditional love

*Purpose:* The promotion of the concept of unconditional love as an attainable ideal. To spread knowledge and understanding of this concept with its underlying premises as we (1) accept full responsibility for all of our feelings, thoughts, actions and choices, and as we (2), in a safe environment, release negative emotions that we repressed in the past, we can live free, happy, and loving lives, at peace with ourselves and others.

*Facilities:* Our office here in Headwaters is concerned principally with administrative matters: coordinating various workshops, publishing the newsletter, filling mail orders, and answering correspondence. We do not have a hospice here, nor do we have any AIDS babies at our center. We are in the process, however, of finding homes for babies infected with AIDS.

*Services:* We offer workshops to all ages which allow participants to express past pains, evaluate the results, and develop new patterns of living. Programs available through the center include: 5-day life, death, and transition workshops conducted by Elisabeth Kübler-Ross, M.D., and/or staff; 3-day follow-up intensive workshops; training programs in the "externalization" process which promote quality support and caring for the whole person; 3-day teenage workshops; 1-day children's workshops.

*Visions and Goals:* To live the message of our purpose and to spread it far and wide. We believe that as individuals hear, experience the truth of this message, and live it themselves, all of life will become increasingly rich in the values all people inherently cherish.

*Materials Available:* Quarterly newsletter distributed to members upon receipt of an annual subscription. Membership also includes a mail order catalog selling books, booklets, tapes, and videos.

*Miscellaneous:* We are a growing network of concerned people with projects and programs serving various community needs. Many of our local groups (listed under "Friends of EKR") meet regularly. If you are interested, please write or call your local group for information on its activities.

# Association for Research and Enlightenment, Inc.

67th Street and Atlantic Avenue, Virginia Beach, VA 23451
(804) 428-3588

*Hours:* 9:00 a.m.–5:00 p.m., 7 days a week
*Person to Contact:* Kevin Todeschi
*Founder:* Edgar Cayce (1931)
*Owner:* Corporation
*Purpose:* To make available information that came through psychic Edgar Cayce and to apply that information.
*Facilities:* Library, visitor center, university, massotherapy school, and bookstore.
*Services:* Seminars, conferences, and lectures.
*Visions and Goals:* To make manifest the love of God and man.
*Materials Available:* Books.

# Indian Valley Retreat

Route 2, Box 58, Willis, VA 24380
(703) 789-4295

*Hours:* 24 hours a day, 7 days a week
*Person to Contact:* Tom and Ise Williams, Owners
*Founder/Owner:* Tom and Ise Williams (summer 1982)
*Purpose:* To offer workshops and classes in a nurturing and healing atmosphere, encompassing a wide variety of self-help discovery avenues that enable persons to go deeper into themselves and bring back tools for self-growth and transformation.
*Facilities:* One hundred forty acres of rolling hills, mountain streams, and gardens, cabins for retreats, and dormitory-style overnight accommodations. Workshops are held in a large, new building.
*Services:* We offer individual retreats (structured or nonstructured), and we also rent our facilities out to like-minded groups or businesses. We offer individual sessions in transformational counseling, massage therapy, and nutritional counseling. We also offer an annual Women's Wellness Week.
*Visions and Goals:* To provide a peaceful and tranquil backdrop to the workshops and retreats.

# More Centers/Retreats

### Florida

*Mark-Age/Healing Haven*    P.O. Box 290368, Ft. Lauderdale, FL 33329
(305-587-5555)

*A Private Place*    309 Lomisa Street, Key West, FL 33040 (305-294-7709)

*Center Associates*    1025 1st Avenue N., St. Petersburg, FL 33705
(813-894-6564)

### Georgia

*Chrysalis at Kingswood*    Box 725, Clayton, GA 30525 (404-782-4278)

### North Carolina

*Essence Light Center*    3427 Denson Place, Charlotte, NC 28215

*Polestar Retreat Center*    604 Mt. Vernon Avenue, Charlotte, NC 28203

*Human Dimensions Institute and Center*    Rural Route 1, Box 1420,
Columbus, NC 28722

*Durham Yoga & Meditation Center*    1214 Broad Street, #2, Durham,
NC 27705 (919-342-0208)

*Moonfire Retreat Center*    Route 1, Box 171B, Durham, NC 27705
(919-490-1849)

*Wellsprings Farm*    5855 Yadlinville Road, Pfafftown, NC 27040
(919-922-4082)

### South Carolina

*Piedmont Yoga Center*    186 E. Main Street, Pendleton, SC 29670
(803-646-7002)

### Virginia

*The Mystical Path*    Box 3055, Alexandria, VA 22302 (703-978-1534)

*Friends of EKR*    Route 5, Box 315-AB, Charlottesville, VA 22901
(804-977-8927)

*The Homestead*    Hot Springs, VA 24445 (703-839-5500)

*Sevenoaks Center*    Route 1, Box 86, Madison, VA 22727 (703-948-6544)

*Friends of EKR*    Route 2, Box 481, Marshall, VA 22115 (703-364-3195)

*Friends of EKR*    17 Regis Circle, Sterling, VA 22170 (703-450-6290)

*By-the-Sea*　218 43rd Street, Virginia Beach, VA 23451
　(804-428-1644)
*The Greenbrier*　White Sulphur Spring, VA 24986 (304-536-1110)

**West Virginia**
*The Kotaka Center*　354 High Street, Morgantown, WV 26505
　(304-292-8539)

# Part XI: Canada

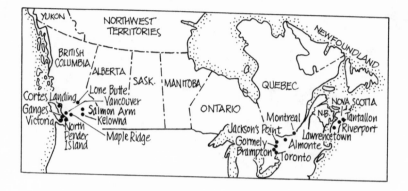

# Hollyhock

Box 127, Manson's Landing, Cortes Island, British Columbia V0P 1K0
(604) 935-6465

*Hours:* Open from April to October
*Founder/Owner:* Rex Weyler, Shivon and Lee Robinsong (1981)
*Purpose:* Hollyhock is a community and a conference center that
since 1982 has provided quality educational courses, retreats, and
natural inspiration to our summer guests.
*Facilities:* Located on 23 acres of beachfront property in a pristine
island setting. The lodge looks south along the Strait of George.
Some private rooms, orchard cabins, and a main accommodation
center, plus two circular, skylighted workshop buildings surrounded
by towering fir and cedar trees. Hot tub and spectacular beach
setting.
*Services:* Offering five-day and weekend workshops in the practical,
creative, and healing arts. Diverse range of workshops available, couples, spirituality, professional upgrading in the healing arts, meditation, retreats, writing, singing, and much more. Morning yoga and
meditation classes. Fine vegetarian and seafood cuisine served.

# Rainbow Center for Attitudinal Healing

785 Cactus Road, Kelowna, British Columbia V1X 3N5
(604) 860-7414

*Hours:* 9:00 a.m.–5:00 p.m., Monday–Friday
*Person to Contact:* Norma Selbie, President
*Founder:* Established in 1981, as one of numerous attitudinal healing
centers around North America
*Owner:* Nonprofit, nonsectarian, tax-exempt organization
*Purpose:* To supplement traditional health care by providing an
environment in which children with catastrophic illness, along
with their families, actively participate in the process of attitudinal
healing.
*Services:* Our services are free. We exist on voluntary contributions of
time, money, and love from individuals and community organizations.
*Visions and Goals:* Attitudinal healing is a process of choosing inner
peace and letting go of painful and fearful attitudes. When we let go
of fear only love remains. We believe love is the most important healing force in the world. Despite the terrors and anxieties of severe illness, we can learn to live in greater peace and harmony through love
and forgiveness.

# Salt Spring Centre (for the Creative and Healing Arts)

Box 1133, Ganges, British Columbia V0S 1E0
(604) 537-2326

*Hours:* 9:00 a.m.–6:00 p.m., Monday–Friday
*Person to Contact:* Sid Fickow, Centre Director
*Founder/Owner:* Dharma Sara Satsang Society (July 1981)
*Purpose:* To establish a peaceful environment in which to carry on
(1) the practices of Ashtanga yoga by a residential community; (2) a
center for the creative arts—painting, pottery, theater—and the
healing arts; (3) organic gardening and orchard techniques; (4) alternative school, kindergarten through 6th grade.
*Facilities:* The Salt Spring Centre is situated on 69 beautiful acres of
woods and meadows with 1½ acres of cultivated organic garden,
large greenhouse, and access to Blackburn Lake for swimming. The
main program house has a large program area of approximately 1,500
square feet, a full-size kitchen and dining area, bedroom and suite
on the main floor, and seven bedrooms on the upper floor. The
upper-floor bedrooms sleep two to four persons each and have
shared bathrooms. Additional dormitory and wood sauna available.
Three delicious vegetarian meals a day provided. Swedon (herbal
steam box). Facilities and services are available for rent to group
leaders in the healing and creative arts.
*Services:* Weekends of rest and relaxation. Health holidays, women's
weekends, slimming weekends and "Going Deeper." Evening classes.
Health treatments including reflexology, Swedon, and polarity.
*Visions and Goals:* To expand the school program to run through high
school. To expand healing services and guest facilities to include
sulfur water hot tubs, a full clinic, and year-round healing retreat
facility. To extend healing retreat times. To complete vegetarian
cookbook.
*Miscellaneous:* Seed company and garden nursery operated in association with the Centre. The school's evening programs teach govern-
ment curriculum with emphasis on and respect for individuality,
problem solving, and respect for the environment. The classes are
small and nonsectarian.

# Dream of the Forest

R.R. 1, Lone Butte, British Columbia V0K 1X0
(604) 593-4603

*Person to Contact:* Hans Terlingen, M.D.
*Founder/Owner:* Hans, Anne Mieke, Meleana, Miranda and Melissa
Terlingen (1977)
*Purpose:* A place for growth, learning, and healing.
*Facilities:* A homestead of almost 500 acres in the mountains of central British Columbia. The main log house is set along a small river, with wood-heated sauna downstream. We can accommodate a total of twelve guests in the main house and three cabins. Hiking trails cross the property, linking several lakes.
*Services:* The "Body and Soul" workshop, a simple and practical approach to learning the skills of relaxation, visualization, and meditation. The two-day retreat is held 3 to 4 times a year starting on a Friday. A retreat for people who want/need a quiet spot somewhere.
*Miscellaneous:* The quiet forest becomes an inspiration, for learning and seeing.

# Touchstone Centre

12084 211th Street, Maple Ridge, British Columbia V2X 8K8
(604) 463-9879

*Hours:* 10:00 a.m.–10:00 p.m., Monday–Friday
*Person to Contact:* Janice Dowson, Director
*Founder/Owner:* Janice Dowson (October 1978)
*Purpose:* To support people in using internal resources to continue the healing process.
*Services:* Individual consultations, couples therapy, group therapy, women's group, treatment marathons, workshops on topics such as spirituality, past life regression, and stages of development, transactional analysis training, and corrective parenting workshops.
*Visions and Goals:* Continue to support the community in social change and planetary awareness.

# Gardom Lake International Earth Friendship Center

(at the Twin Island Resort)
P.O. Box 7, Salmon Arm, British Columbia V1E 4N2
(Street address: Gardom Lake Road, 3.2 miles west off Highway 97B)
(604) 838-7587

*Hours:* 8:00 a.m.–9:00 p.m., Monday–Friday

*Person to Contact:* Sarah Kipp

*Founder/Owner:* Sarah Kipp and Clive Callaway (January 1988)

*Purpose:* To foster both personal and planetary wellness through the provision of courses, workshops, retreats, and experiential vacations in a holistic setting that offers learning, adventure, relaxation, and recreation consistent with the Earth Friendship Center concept. The fundamental principle underlying Earth Friendship Centers is the integrating of personal wellness and planetary wellness. When we heal ourselves, we heal the earth. When we heal the earth, we heal ourselves.

*Facilities:* Twelve self-contained lakeside housekeeping cottages, 8 shaded camping sites, bed and breakfast at the main house, central meeting lounge, meditation room/resource center, beach, canoe, boat and bicycle rentals, nearby hiking, and cross-country ski trails in the winter. A central lodge and a dining center are being planned.

*Services:* A variety of workshops and courses, body work/massage therapy, intuitive and personal counseling, guided nature walks with interpretive biologist, office services (photocopying, word processing, graphics and design studio), airport, bus and train pickup, organized "adventure" tours, hot springs, winery tours, and backcountry hiking.

*Visions and Goals:* The Earth Friendship Center concept provides our central vision, that is, that there is a strong connection between personal and earth wellness. In order to help heal the environment, we need to transform our ways of being, and the Center is oriented to facilitating this transformation, always with our connection to the Earth being fundamental.

*Materials Available:* Brochure and information flyer on the Earth Friendship Center concept. Newsletter. Workshop and program calendar. Resource center.

*Miscellaneous:* This is a pilot project on the Earth Friendship Center concept. The concept is transferable and any group can adopt it.

# Other Dimensions Training Center

Box 2269, Salmon Arm, British Columbia V1E 4R3
(604) 832-8483

*Hours:* 8:30 a.m.–5:00 p.m., Monday–Saturday

*Person to Contact:* Jeanie, Administrative Assistant, or Andy and Bonnie Schneider, Directors

*Founder/Owner:* Andy Schneider (January 1984)

*Purpose:* To serve humanity according to the highest principles of the New Age. To bring about a greater integration of the body, mind, soul, and spirit within each individual. To increase the harmony between all people and all levels of being under the guidance of divine will. The esoteric training hastens the evolutionary process of unfolding growth.

*Facilities:* Spacious meeting room, sleeping accommodations for 30, large fully equipped kitchen, dining area seating 60, in-house library, bookstore, audiotape and videotape center, sauna, volleyball court, horseshoe pits, nearby beaches for swimming, therapy room, and administrative office.

*Services:* Retreats, private or groups. Workshops and seminars— spiritual, metaphysical, esoteric, or personal and psychological growth. Meditation groups. Sacred circle dance. Training program in esoteric studies, three-year core program. Certification in teaching, healing and counseling. The center is available to rent for workshops, seminars, or retreats.

*Visions and Goals:* To be a center for specialized training in the holistic disciplines of the ancient wisdom and all types of activities and learning that improve the quality of life in all departments of human living.

*Materials Available:* New Age books, tapes, and metaphysical supplies. Center Light newspaper. Esoteric studies videotapes.

*Miscellaneous:* The center is located near the Trans-Canada Highway, 12 km (7.5 mi.) west of Salmon Calgary. The location of the center provides a peaceful country atmosphere in a woodland setting near scenic Shuswap Lake.

# Clam Bay Farm

R.R. #1, North Pender Island, British Columbia V0N 2M0
(604) 629-6313
*Person to Contact:* Corrine Davis, Manager
*Founder/Owner:* North Shore Free Press (1981)
*Purpose:* To provide a peaceful and nurturing environment for the study of the practical and healing arts.
*Facilities:* Organic farm on 100 acres located on ½-mile ocean shoreline in Canada's Gulf Islands. Meals cooked with our own produce and preserves. Shared accommodations. Small lake for fishing, swimming, canoeing. Horses, walking trails, hot tub, and sauna. Meeting space in beautiful lakeside gazebo.
*Services:* Weekend and weeklong workshops and retreats. Information available on request. Available to groups for workshops, seminars, and retreats. Transportation service from Pender Island ferry dock.

# The Centre for Human Growth

1819 Quebec Street, Vancouver, British Columbia V5T 2Z3
(604) 876-0800

*Hours:* 12:00 noon–10:00 p.m., Monday–Friday (plus some weekends)
*Person to Contact:* Jean Sabina, Manager/Owner
*Founder/Owner:* Jean Sabina (August 1987, opened January 1988)
*Purpose:* To provide an environment for each individual to explore aspects of the self on all four levels to gain insight and acceptance of his or her own existence and relationship to the universal environment.
*Facilities:* Two seminar rooms, practitioner's office, lounge and small retail business office, coffee facilities, and library.
*Services:* Courses (short and long), workshops, seminars, healing, lending library, art gallery.
*Visions and Goals:* Full-time school/center with multiple offerings—all learner-centered programs with top-quality facilitators.

# Inner Garden Activity Centre/Reflexology Centre of Vancouver

535 West 10th Avenue, Vancouver, British Columbia V5Z 1K9
(604) 875-8818

*Hours:* 10:00 a.m.–5:00 p.m., Monday–Friday
*Person to Contact:* Chris Shirley, Director/Owner
*Founder:* Chris Shirley (December 1983)
*Purpose:* To provide a safe space for personal growth and natural healing on physical, emotional, psychological, and spiritual levels and to give an introduction and promotion of alternative modes of healing.
*Facilities:* Daytime: practitioner's office, office, and small reading library. Weekends and evenings: seminar rooms, both small and large.
*Services:* Weekend workshops and evening classes in a variety of areas including reflexology and psychic awareness/healing. Friday evening presentations of a variety of health-oriented topics and practices. Lazaris video showings on Thursday evenings, and private sessions with practitioners in the daytime.
*Materials Available:* Massage tables, reflexology books, charts, sandals, rollers, Lazaris books, audio- and videotapes for rent or sale.

# Preventive Medicine

3743 W. 10th Avenue, Vancouver, British Columbia
(604) 228-1022

*Hours:* 8:00 a.m.–5:00 p.m., Monday–Friday
*Person to Contact:* Dr. R. Winona Rowat
*Founder/Owner:* Michael Sharzer and R. Winona Rowat
*Purpose:* To spread information, raise awareness of self-responsibility, act as a liaison, and educate.
*Facilities:* Pleasant, large, casual offices and massage room and healing room. Three doctors and massage therapist.
*Services:* Health counseling and maintenance, massage, general practitioners in whole health orientation.
*Visions and Goals:* To teach medical students more than is shown on television.
*Materials Available:* Books and periodicals.

# Dispensable Healing Center

403 Kingston Street, Victoria, British Columbia V8V 1V8
(604) 384-5560

*Hours:* 9:00 a.m.–5:00 p.m., Monday–Friday
*Person to Contact:* Sabina Pettitt
*Founder/Owner:* Sabina and Michael Pettitt (1982)
*Purpose:* Attitudinal healing.
*Facilities:* Small treatment and workshop space.
*Services:* Workshops and individual sessions. Regular courses on A Course in Miracles.
*Visions and Goals:* Teach only love.
*Materials Available:* Produce flower, sea, and gem essences in association with Pacific Essences.

# The L.I.F.E. Project

209 Henry Street, Victoria, British Columbia V9A 3H8
(604) 384-2146

*Hours:* 24 hours a day, 7 days a week
*Person to Contact:* Roberta Scothorne, Executive Director
*Founder/Owner:* Roberta Scothorne (October 1987)
*Purpose:* To offer the principles of attitudinal healing to anyone wishing to enhance the quality of life and to support those in transition. Following the work of Dr. Jampolsky and A Course in Miracles.
*Facilities:* Meeting rooms in main building (soon to have a rural seaside retreat center as well).
*Services:* Evening drop-in groups; private counseling; A Course in Miracles study groups.
*Visions and Goals:* We are committed to helping one another achieve the shift in perception from fear to love, from conflict to inner peace.
*Materials Available:* Visions for Children tape series (16 tapes); *Reaching and Teaching*, a manual for teaching self-awareness to children ages 5 to 12.

# Victoria Stress Centre

5575 W. Saanich Road, R.R. 5, Victoria, British Columbia V8X 4M6
(604) 727-3451

*Hours:* 9:00 a.m.–4:30 p.m., Monday–Friday
*Person to Contact:* Sally Kaye
*Founder:* Dr. P. Nunn and Heather Nunn (March 1980)
*Owner:* Dr. and Mrs. Kaye and Dr. and Mrs. Nunn
*Purpose:* We specialize in "no treatment" programs for burnout, chronic pain, cancer, addictions, and so forth. We take you seriously and want to take you to a place of clarity for yourself.
*Facilities:* Sixteen beds in country-style living on 5 acres, with a tennis court and vegetable garden.
*Services:* Outpatient and intensive residential programs, including self-respect and addiction programs, and one-to-one counseling.
*Visions and Goals:* Development of personalized life-style change programs.
*Materials Available:* Brochures. Workshop leaders available.

# Ledgehill Retreat and Study Centre

R.R. 1, Lawrencetown, Nova Scotia B0S 1M0
(902) 584-7124

*Hours:* 9:00 a.m.–5:00 p.m., Monday–Friday
*Person to Contact:* Charles E. Bower, Owner
*Founder/Owner:* Charles E. Bower (July 1986)
*Purpose:* Ledgehill is an oasis for people with new ideas, a center where these ideas can be expressed and tested. Offering a quiet country space where groups can meet, Ledgehill is a place of relaxation, peace, quiet sharing of ideas and healthy positive living.
*Facilities:* A 10-room, 70-year-old Victorian-style house. Situated on 110 acres with open fields, mature maples, and forest surrounding the center.
*Services:* Workshops offered throughout the year on various subjects. Food provided. Ledgehill can be rented by certain groups of up to 30.
*Visions and Goals:* To help heal the world and be a center where positive loving energy, good food, and healthy living is practiced.

# The Ovens Natural Park

P.O. Box 38, Riverport, Nova Scotia B0J 2W0
(902) 766-4621

*Hours:* 9:00 a.m.–5:00 p.m., Monday–Friday
*Person to Contact:* Nancy Sherwood
*Founder/Owner:* Nancy Sherwood, David Cameron, and Stephen Chapin (1987)
*Purpose:* To be in harmony with the land and to strive toward oneness through our provision of opportunities for wellness, personal growth, spiritual development, community and creative endeavors.
*Facilities:* 200-acre park on oceanside cliffs. Hiking trails, scuba diving, fishing, dining/workshop space, housekeeping cabins, wooded tent sites, serviced RV spaces, pool, family-style meals (in summer).
*Services:* Workshops, channeling, full moon meditation, musical events, sweat lodge, massage by appointment, hermitage, and space available for works of artists, craftspeople and artisans.
*Visions and Goals:* To preserve and protect the natural, historical features and wonders of this land and to expand in fulfillment of our purpose.
*Materials Available:* Craft shop offering books, crystals, herbals, jewelry, and native baskets. A small provisions store.

## Akala Point

Box 4, Site 28, R.R. 1, Tantallon, Nova Scotia B0J 3J0
(902) 823-2160

*Hours:* 8:00 a.m.–6:00 p.m,. 7 days a week
*Person to Contact:* Gerry Barbor, Manager
*Founder/Owner:* Barbara Jannasch (1985)
*Purpose:* The focus at Akala Point is on respectful attention to ourselves; to mind, body, and spirit; to our work and play; and our con-
nectedness with the whole of humanity. The people at Akala Point
wish to preserve and enhance the prevailing energies and make
them available to all people of goodwill.
*Facilities:* Main building includes the "Big Room" with ocean view,
fireplace, quality sound system, and piano, and kitchen with modern commercial equipment, dining area, and deck with ocean view.
Older Cape-Cod style cottage, also with ocean view, which accommodates up to 10. Office lounge and staff residence. Vegetarian food
served, organic garden, small sandy beach, and rocky ocean frontage.
*Services:* Courses available; gestalt groups, inroads through dreams,
movement, breath therapy, dance, organic gardening, stress reduction, vegetarian cooking, and yoga.

## Macrobiotics Canada

R.R. 3, Almonte, Ontario K0A 1A0
(613) 256-2665

*Hours:* 7:00 a.m.–6:00 p.m., Monday–Friday
*Person to Contact:* Wayne Diotte, Director
*Founder/Owner:* Wayne Diotte (1979)
*Purpose:* Macrobiotics Canada is an educational and self-healing center involved in nationwide macrobiotic education, personal and relationship counseling, and mail order books, food and cookware.
*Facilities:* Beautiful location by the Mississippi River in the Ottawa Valley, with pure water and delicious air. Can accommodate 40-50 people.
*Services:* Services include: educational seminars conducted throughout Canada, macrobiotic consultations and information sessions
with approved teachers, relationship and family counseling, cooking
classes, intensive study sessions, Macrobiotic Teacher Training Program, Annual Summer Study/Fun Camp, Macrobiotic Meditation
Weekends.
*Visions and Goals:* To make the Macrobiotic quality of living and
thinking available to all. Macrobiotics is a way of approaching life. It
offers a large view, a way of perceiving, pursuing, creating, and living
"A Great Life'"—full of energy, good humor, and adventure.

# Positive Alternative Wellness Center

123 Queen Street West, Brampton, Ontario L6Y 1M3
(416) 454-2688

*Hours:* 9:00 a.m.–5:00 p.m., Monday–Friday
*Person to Contact:* Mary Simpson, Director
*Founder/Owner:* Mary Simpson, R.N., C.A.C. (1983)
*Purpose:* Promotion of holistic/wellness concepts. Encouragement of self-responsibility in health.
*Facilities:* Office, small meeting room, with the capacity for 12 to 15 people.
*Services:* Holistic wellness consultations, relaxation-stress management, therapeutic touch, imagery, addictions counseling/education, variety of workshops in self-awareness/transformational techniques, and instruction in therapeutic touch (Krieger).
*Miscellaneous:* Rental to other health care professionals provides additional alternative/complementary therapies (psychotherapy, homeopathy, colon therapy).


# Chestnut Hill, Inc.

P.O. Box 454, R.R. 1, Gormley, Ontario L0H 1G0
(416) 888-1231

*Hours:* 8:00 a.m.–8:00 p.m., Monday–Friday
*Person to Contact:* Katharine Kunz
*Founder/Owner:* Katharine Kunz (May 1982)
*Purpose:* Chestnut Hill offers an opportunity to leave stress and tension behind. Renew vital energy. Relax and rejuvenate in a beautiful country atmosphere.
*Facilities:* Fifty acres of gardens, fields, and trees overlooking its own spring-fed lake. Beautiful resident building with 15 beds, one and two to a room. A spacious living-dining area with glass walls overlooks the lake. Sauna, whirlpool, and mineral therapy bath.
*Services:* Juice fasting plus low calorie meals, massage therapy, reflexology, and facials. Stretch classes that focus on flexibility and relaxation techniques.
*Visions and Goals:* Construction of more rooms has already begun. Our outdoor swimming pool and more service rooms were completed fall 1988.

## Artemisia Institute for Botanical, Medical and Preventative Health Care Education

Box 190, Jackson's Point, Ontario L0E 1L0
(416) 722-8604

*Hours:* 8:00 a.m.–5:00 p.m., Monday–Friday
*Person to Contact:* Christine E. Devai, Owner
*Founder/Owner:* Christine E. Devai (spring 1977)
*Purpose:* Provide public alternative self-education, without dogma.
*Facilities:* Gardens, schoolroom, offices, treatment rooms, and dispensary.
*Services:* Counseling, classes, workshops, seminars, and long-term retreats covering such subjects as: alchemy, aromatheraphy, eclectic herbology, herbal cultivation, midwifery, Native Indian herbology, nutrition, philosophy of natural healing, remedial exercises.
*Visions and Goals:* To broaden public awareness toward personal and collective health responsibility and freedom.


## Toronto Healing Arts Centre

715 Bloor Street West, Toronto, Ontario M6G 1L5
(416) 535-8777

*Hours:* Answering service available all hours
*Person to Contact:* Nicholas Ashfield
*Founder/Owner:* Nicholas Ashfield
*Purpose:* To provide a home environment for excellent wholistic therapists to independently practice their work.
*Facilities:* Two houses side by side near subway. Comforting ambience of home with 15 treatment rooms.
*Services:* Chiropractic massage, acupuncture, nutritional counseling, radionics, psychotherapy, reflexology, shiatsu, and aesthetic services.
*Materials Available:* Bookstore on premises with a variety of healing books and a crystal gallery.

# The Wyebridge Centre

74 Madison Avenue, Toronto, Ontario M5R 2S4
(416) 924-9070

*Hours:* 7:00 a.m.–10:00 p.m., 7 days a week
*Person to Contact:* June Zelonka, Director
*Founder/Owner:* June Zelonka, M.A., and Bronek Zelonka, M.D.
*Purpose:* To facilitate deep relaxation, self-awareness, regeneration, and creative self-expression.
*Facilities:* Double accommodations in tastefully restored historic lodge on parklike grounds. A cottage on a sandy beach with excellent swimming in Lake Huron. Outdoor hot tub. A specialized library of books and tapes. Delicious vegetarian meals served.
*Services:* A health spa program, fasting and meditation retreats, relaxation therapy groups for relief of stress, anxiety, and chronic pain. Weekends and 5-day format. Yoga based stretching, Trager and Esalen Massage. Individual and group self-exploration sessions through imagery, meditation, dream work, movement, breathing, and music.

# Health Training Group

(Montreal Clinic and Head Office)
3789 Hampton Avenue, Montreal, Quebec H4A 2K7
(514) 485-6373

*Hours:* 9:00 a.m.–5:00 p.m., Monday–Friday
*Founder/Owner:* Howard Kiewe and Gayle Lang (January 1979)
*Purpose:* To teach transformation and healing of body, mind, and spirit.
*Facilities:* The health training group is a network of health care professionals. The Montreal office has a clinical facility used for private therapy. Seminars are given in Ottawa (224-6446), Toronto (221-2992), Calgary (229-3681), and Vancouver (224-1160).
*Services:* Offer private sessions, basic workshops, and complete professional training in polarity therapy, rebirthing, prosperity principles, and related topics. Regular seminars in all the cities mentioned above.
*Materials Available:* Books and audiotapes on relevant topics.

# More Centers/Retreats

### Alberta
*Calgary Esoteric Philosophy Centre*   2127 Broadway N.W., Calgary, Alberta
*Friends of EKR*   4858 32nd Avenue, Edmonton, Alberta T6L 4H0 (403-463-8695)
*Center for Attitudinal Healing*   150 Willow Street, Sherwood Park, Alberta P8A 1P4

### British Columbia
*Atlin Holistic Health Centre*   Box 284, Atlin, B.C. V0W 1A (604-651-7655)
*The Salt Springs Clinic*   Box 4, Fulford Harbour, B.C. V0S 1C0 (604-653-4216)
*Bright Farm*   R.R. 1, Tripp Road, Ganges, B.C. V0S 1E0 (604-537-2378)
*Taurus Farm Bed 'n Breakfast*   Box 1543, Ganges, B.C. V0S 1E0 (604-537-4076)
*Friends of EKR*   1261 Colombia Street, Kamloops, B.C. V2C 2W4 (604-374-7239)
*Hailos Wholistic Living Society*   Box 8, Lumby, B.C. V0E 2G0 (604-547-9680)
*Canadian Attitudinal Healing Center*   3589 Granville Street, Vancouver, B.C. V6H 3K5 (604-736-7112)
*Friends of EKR*   6190 MacDonald Street, Vancouver, B.C. V6N 1E6 (604-261-6422)
*Preventive Medicine Society*   3743 10th Avenue, Vancouver, B.C. (604-224-1515)
*Vancouver Art of Living Center*   1664 Broadway Street, Vancouver, B.C. (604-736-2428)
*Islands Holistic Association*   1126A Dallas Road, Victoria, B.C. V8W 1T8 (604-389-1290)
*Self-Health Herbal Centre*   1221 Wharf Street, Victoria, B.C. V8W 1T8 (604-383-1913)
*Victoria Attunement Centre*   Suite 1, 2727 Quadra Street, Victoria, B.C. V8T 4E5 (604-383-1243)

### Manitoba
*Winnipeg Center for Attitudinal Healing*   P.O. Box 1, St. Norbert, Manitoba R3V 1L5 (204-269-1502)
*Friends of EKR*   225 Hill Street, Winnipeg, Manitoba R2H 2L7 (204-233-2854)

*Friends of EKR*    405-421 Assiniboine Avenue, Winnipeg, Manitoba
R3C 0Y4 (204-772-9055)

**Ontario**

*Santosa Yoga and Health Centre*    16A Wyndham, Guelph, Ontario
N1H 4E5 (519-837-3022)

*Life Space Holistic Center*    1527 Davenport Road, Toronto, Ontario
M6H 2H9 (416-533-1903)

*Toronto Health Education Centre*    258 Dupont Street, Toronto,
Ontario M5R 1V7 (416-926-1788)

*West End Holistic Centre*    12 Heintzman Street, Toronto, Ontario
M6P 2J6 (416-763-3211)

# Publications

**The Northwest**
*Transformational Times*
Box 425, Beavercreek, OR 97004
(503) 632-7141
Bimonthly/Free

*New Age Information Service*
Box 1043, Corvallis, OR 97330

*Connections Journal and Resource Directory*
P.O. Box 10367, Eugene, OR 97440-2367
(503) 683-1935

*Fresh Life Guide*
P.O. Box 02586, Portland, OR 97202
(503) 236-3037

*Reflections Directory*
P.O. Box 13070, Portland, OR 97213
(503) 281-4486
Quarterly/Free

*Life Quest Network*
P.O. Box 26, Salem, OR 97308

*Connections*
1266 L Street, Springfield, OR 97477

*Common Ground-Puget Sound*
Box 15519, Seattle, WA 98115-0519
(206) 443-9504

*Holistic Resources, Inc.*
P.O. Box 3653, Seattle, WA 98124-3653
(206) 523-2101

*Insight Northwest*
Box 95341, Seattle, WA 98145-2341

*The New Times*
Box 51186, Seattle, WA 98115
(206) 524-9071
Monthly/Free or Subscription

*Washington Living*
4141 California Avenue S.W., Seattle, WA 98116

**The Pacific**
*Alaskan Well-Being*
Box 104552, Anchorage, AL 99510

*New You! Positive Lifestyle Magazine*
Box 89068, Honolulu, HI 96830
(808) 942-3786
Quarterly/Subscription

*Massage Magazine*
Box 1389-MB, Kailua, Kona, HI 96745
(808) 329-2433

*Common Ground Hawaii*
47-155 Okana Road, Kaneohe, HI 96744
(808) 239-7190

**California**
*NAM/New Ager Mailing Lists*
P.O. Box 1067, Berkeley, CA 94701
(415) 644-3229

*Shaman's Drum*
P.O. Box 2636, Berkeley, CA 94702
(415) 525-5122
Quarterly/Subscription

*Yoga Journal*
2054 University Avenue, Berkeley, CA 94704
(415) 841-9200
Bimonthly/Subscription

*The Light Connection*
Box 578, Cardiff by the Sea, CA 92007
(619) 944-1005
Monthly/Subscription

*Natural New Age Yellow Pages*
Box 5978A, Fullerton, CA 92635
(800) 541-0900

*L.A. Resources & Orange County Resources*
228 20th Street, Huntington Beach, CA 92648
(714) 969-1371
Quarterly/Free

*Southern California's New Age Telephone Book*
2305 Canyon Drive, Los Angeles, CA 90068
(213) 469-4454
Annually/Free

*Holistic Health*
Box 955, Mill Valley, CA 94942

*Common Ground*
305 San Anselmo Avenue, Suite 217, San Anselmo, CA 94960
(415) 459-4900
Quarterly/Free

*Wholistic Living News*
Box 16346, San Diego, CA 92116
(619) 280-0317
Monthly/Subscription

*Magical Blend*
Box 11303, San Francisco, CA 94101-7303
(415) 673-1001
Quarterly/Subscription

*New Dimensions*
P.O. Box 410510, San Francisco, CA 94141
Bimonthly/Subscription

*Spiritual Community Guide*
Box 1080, San Rafael, CA 94902
(415) 863-4788

*Life Times*
Box 4129, Santa Barbara, CA 93140
(805) 962-9949
Quarterly/Subscription

*Source Net*
Box 6767, Santa Barbara, CA

*Spectrum*
4724 Thurber Lane, Santa Cruz, CA 95065

*Whole Life Times*
409 Santa Monica Boulevard, Santa Monica, CA 90401
(213) 395-7701
Monthly/Subscription

*Essential Whole Earth Catalogue*
27 Gate-Five Road, Sausalito, CA 94965

*Well-Being Community Calendar*
P.O. Box 819, Sebastopol, CA 95473
(707) 887-7854
Monthly/Free

*Meditation Magazine*
17510 Sherman Way, Van Nuys, CA 91406

**The Southwest**
*New World-New Age Directory*
P.O. Box 17029, Fountain Hills, AZ 85268
(602) 230-3600
Quarterly/Subscription

*Omega New-Age Directory*
6418 S. 39th Avenue, Phoenix, AZ 85041
(602) 253-1223
Monthly/Subscription

*Arizona Networking News*
6333 E. Thunderbird Road, Scottsdale, AZ 85254

*Tucson Lifeline*
Box 44028, Tucson, AZ 95733

*Choices and Connections*
P.O. Box 1057, Boulder, CO 80306
(800) 992-9190
Annually/Fee

*Nexus*
1680 6th Street, #6, Boulder, CO 80302

*Celebrations*
2209 W. Colorado Avenue, Colorado Springs, CO 80904
(714) 634-1855
Quarterly/Free

*New Age Network of Colorado Springs*
P.O. Box 6647, Colorado Springs, CO 80934
(303) 634-1855

*Cosmic Connections*
Box 26166, Lakewood, CO 80226
(303) 985-8853

*Erospirit*
Box 35160, Albuquerque, NM 87176

*Crosswinds*
P.O. Box 39, Santa Fe, NM 87504
Monthly/Subscription

*Transformations Santa Fe Reporter*
322 Montezuma Avenue, Santa Fe, NM 87501
(505) 988-5541

## The Plains
*Innerworld*
Box 30054, St. Louis, MO 63119
(314) 822-7134
Monthly/Subscription

## The South
*New Texas Magazine*
4408 Marathon, Austin, TX 78756
(512) 453-0515

*Inner-connection*
P.O. Box 780638, Dallas, TX 75378
(214) 696-3159
Monthly/Free

## The Midwest
*Heartland*
7000 N. Glenwood, Chicago, IL 60626

*The Institute for Earth Education*
Box 288, Warrenville, IL 60555

*phenomeNEWS*
28545 Greenfield, Suite 111, Southfield, MI 48076
(313) 569-3888
Monthly/Subscription

*Greater Cincinnati Resource Directory*
3514 Burch Street, Cincinnati, OH 45208

*Realities Unlimited*
520 University, #115, Madison, WI 53703
(608) 256-0080

## New England
*New Age Journal*
342 Western Avenue, Brighton, MA 02135-1095
(617) 787-2005
Bimonthly/Subscription

*Directory of Holistic Practitioners*
Box 1705, Brookline, MA 02146

*Alternative America*
Box 134, Cambridge, MA 02138

*Contact Quarterly*
P.O. Box 603, Northampton, MA 01061
(413) 232-4377

*Many Hands*
150 Main Street, Northampton, MA 01060
(413) 586-5037
Quarterly/Free

*New Visions*
10 Taconic Street, Pittsfield, MA 01201

*Earthstar/New England*
Box 1597, Meredith, NH 03253
(603) 279-7429

**Mid-Atlantic**
*The Door Opener*
70 Valley Falls Road, Vernon, CT 06066
(203) 875-4101
Quarterly/Subscription

*Travelers Network Magazine*
7501 Sebago Road, Bethesda, MD 20034
(301) 229-2802

*Sources*
P.O. Box 1076-RS, Columbia, MD 21044
(301) 995-1605
Bimonthly/Subscription

*Baltimore Resources*
Box 284, Stevenson, MD 21153
(301) 486-1510
Quarterly/Free

*Pathways*
Box 5719, Tacoma Park, MD 20912
(202) 829-3289

*Free Spirit*
137 Sixth Street, Brooklyn, NY 112176
(718) 638-6990

*Heart and Wings Journal*
Box 574, Lebanon Springs, NY 12114-0586
(518) 766-5344

*Dialogue House*
80 E. 11th Street, New York, NY 10003-6035

*Spa Finder*
784 Broadway, New York, NY 10003
(800) 255-7727

*Whole Life Magazine*
89 5th Avenue, New York, NY 10003

*East West Journal*
Box 6769, Syracuse, NY 13217

*Yoga Journal*
Box 6076, Syracuse, NY 13217
Bimonthly/Subscription

*New Frontier Magazine*
129 N. 13th Street, Philadelphia, PA 19107
(215) 567-1685
Monthly/Subscription

*New Realities*
4000 Albemarle Street N.W., Washington, D.C. 20016
(202) 362-6445
Bimonthly/Subscription

*Pathways*
6926 Willow Street N.W., Washington, D.C. 20012
(202) 829-3289
Quarterly/Free

**The Southeast**
*Mighty Natural Magazine*
P.O. Box 61-1554, North Miami, FL 33261
(305) 893-8829
Monthly/Subscription

*The Natural Yellow Pages*
P.O. Box 61-1554, North Miami, FL 33261
(305) 893-8829
Annually/Fee

*New Age News (New Age Information Network)*
P.O. Box 566714, Atlanta, GA 30356
(404) 255-1369Monthly/Membership

*Alternative Resource Center*
P.O. Box 1707, Forest Park, GA 30050
(404) 361-5823

*Sourcefinder Newsletter*
Box 6232B, Augusta, GA 30906


**Canada**
*New Alberta*
2127 Broadview Road, NM Calgary, Alberta T2N 3J1

*The Networker*
P.O. Box 6769, Station D, Calgary, Alberta T2P 2E6
(403) 253-1310
Bimonthly/Free

*The New Catalyst*
P.O. Box 99, Lilloet, B.C. V0K 1V0
(mobile H42 4955, channel JW)
Quarterly/Subscription

*Common Ground*
Box 34090, Station D, Vancouver, B.C. V6J 4M1
(604) 733-2215
Quarterly/Subscription

*Shared Vision*
Box 34203, Station D, Vancouver, B.C. V6J 4N1

*The New Age Connection*
932 Carter Avenue, Winnipeg, Manitoba R3M 2E3
(204) 452-3656
Quarterly/Free

*Intervox*
Box 2605, Station M, Halifax, Nova Scotia B3J 3W5

*Tone Magazine*
101B Third Avenue, Ottawa, Ontario K1S 2J7
(613) 235-9510
Monthly/Free

*Chimo: The Holistic Magazine for Our Times*
79 Victoria Street, Toronto, Ontario M5C 2B1

*Common Ground Magazine*
67 Baycrest Avenue, Toronto, Ontario M6A 1W2

*Toronto Dimensions*
214 Glengarry Avenue, Toronto, Ontario M5M 1E4
*Les Editions Communiqu'elles*
3585 St. Urbain, Montreal, Quebec H2X 2N6

*Resource Guide*
810 W. Duluth, Montreal, Quebec H2L 1B3

# *Glossary*

*Acupressure*—the application of finger pressure to certain areas of the body, to promote healing. (See Shiatsu)

*Acupuncture*—pricking certain areas of the body with fine needles to promote healing. It is considered by the Chinese to be a form of health maintenance that stimulates the body's ability to sustain and balance itself.

*Aerobics*—the stimulation and relaxation of the body through various physical exercises, often informally set to music.

*Alchemical/alchemy*—essentially a reverence for the material world as being the reflection of a more perfect, living, trancendent reality.

*Alexander technique*—a method encompassing body/mind awareness, conscious control, and organismic thinking.

*Aromatherapy*— an ancient healing art, utilizing the essential oils of herbs and flowers. The oils are used to treat emotional disorders, organ dysfunctions, and skin problems through a variety of application techniques both internally and externally.

*Art therapy*— characterized by the use of symbolic communication presented by graphic, pictorial, sculpted, modeled, collage-composed, or other art media. Art expression involves a confrontation with the psychic images of the realm of inner perception.

*Astrology*—study of the influence of planets (and the heavens) on human psychology, character, and relationships.

*Attitudinal healing*—a concept based on the belief that it is possible to choose peace rather than conflict, love rather than fear.

*Attunement*—to bring the whole person into harmony.

*Ayurveda*—the science of self-healing.

*Bioenergetics*—this psychotherapeutic body work is based on the interconnection between chronic psychological defense mechanisms.

*Biofeedback*—the conscious monitoring of internal body states. It enables people to gain control over some bodily functions previously thought to be "involuntary."

*Body alignment*—developed from the system of Rolfing and includes an in-depth structural analysis and a strengthening and flexibility exercise program.

*Body work*—a broad range of massagelike therapies that retrain the body's posture and movements for optimal functioning.

*Ceremony*—a formal act or set of acts as prescribed by ritual, custom, or etiquette. Comes from the Latin word meaning sacredness.

*Chakra*—seven energy centers on your body. Taken from the Sanskrit word meaning "wheel."

*Channeling*—the art of receiving information, often while in a trance state, from a source, usually someone no longer alive.

*Chiropractic*—analyzes and corrects vertebral spinal nerve interferences and helps to maintain the natural organization of the body so that it can function at its fullest capacity.

*Cleansing*—to free and detoxify one's body from cumulative poisins.

*Colonics/colon hygiene*—an internal bath that washes away toxic waste that builds on the walls of the colon.

*Color healing*—based on the law of attraction wherein the vibration of the color attracts a similar vibration in the human body. Dates back to ancient Egypt and other premodern societies.

*Counseling*—to give advice or guidance.

*Creative visualization*—an effective process of creating what we want in our lives. The art of using mental energy to transform and greatly improve health, beauty, prosperity, loving relationship, and the fulfillments of all one's desires.

*Crystals/crystal healing*—crystals are known to have electromagnetic energy, as does the human body. When a natural quartz crystal is brought into contact with a person's etheric body, the electromagnetic attraction is capable of drawing imbalanced energy out of the human body.

*Dance therapy*—combining self-knowledge and personal analysis with studies in psychotherapy, dance has been rediscovered as a healing art.

*Deep tissue massage*—to realign the body by manipulating the fascia, the connective tissue that envelops the muscles. (See Rolfing)

*Detoxification*—cleansing the body of accumulated poisons often from overtaxation due to addictive habits.

*Eastern medicine*—a holistic perspective on health and illness that sees the relationship of a symptom to the person as a whole, physiologically and psychologically.

*Emotional* —of or pertaining to the expression of feelings.

*Emotional cleansing*—healing and health of the emotional body.

*Energy balancing*—a general term for techniques that channel and stimulate energy in the body.

*Ericksonian hypnosis*—different from traditional hypnosis, the Ericksonian hypnotist takes care not to impose any outside ideas of change on the client but instead carefully reinforces the client's abilities to generate change from within.

*Fasting*—to abstain from certain or all food and certain drink, except water, for a period of time for the purpose of physical detoxification and rejuvenation.

*Feldenkrais method*—two combined techniques that use movement as the medium to explore our habitual movement patterns and bring about new and more efficient states of organization of the self.

*Flotation tank*—a little larger than a twin-size bed, filled with 10 to 12 inches of water, to which great quantities of Epsom salts are added. Floating creates a deep state of relaxation.

*Flower remedies*—directly correlated to specific moods or mental attitudes. Serve as catalysts for the subtler levels of the healing process.

*Gestalt therapy*—meaning "the whole picture," it seeks to resolve incomplete or conflicting gestalts within a person to enable one to be more fully aware and enlivened in the present moment.

*Guided imagery*—a process that involves listening to music or a person's voice in a relaxed state for the purpose of allowing imagery, symbols, and deep feelings to arise from the inner self.

*Hakomi therapy*—a unique approach to personal growth wherein the body is used as a source of information about the unconscious mind, serving as a vehicle to contact those key memories and basic emotional attitudes that determine the overall quality of our daily experience.

*Herbalism/herbology*—the study and use of herbs for healing purposes. Herbs are prepared for internal and external use in a variety of ways including teas, tinctures, extracts, oils, ointments, compresses, and poultices.

*Holistic health*— a perspective on healing that considers all aspects of one's life as creating and comprising a total state of health.

*Homeopathy*—administers substances that most closely produce symptoms manifested by the patient, following the tenet that like cures like. In this way, the body's own vital force is stimulated to cure itself.

*Hot springs*—a place in the earth's surface, often volcanic, where hot mineral waters rise to the surface.

*Hydrotherapy*—medical use of water in the treatment of certain diseases.

*Hypnosis*—inducing an altered state that has been compared to a state of deep meditation or transcendence in which the innate recuperative abilities of the psyche are allowed to flow more freely.

*Hypnotherapy*—may be described as the use of hypnosis as a psychotherapeutic tool.

*Internal medicine*—the medical study and treatment of nonsurgical constitutional diseases in adults.

*Intuitive channeling*—the art of being receptive to "knowing" without the use of rational processes.

*Iridology*—the basic premise of this study is that each organ of the body is represented by an area of the iris.

*Jin shin jyutsu*—a form of energy-balancing massage.

*Jungian therapy*—is based on the work of Carl G. Jung. It focuses on the realization of personality and our search for meaning through the use of dreams, symbols, journals, and Jung's particular theory of basic human archetypes to explore the unconscious.

*Kinesiology*—diagnosing and treating a disease through muscle testing. Virtually any disease state of the body will have a structural manifestation, a specific "body language," represented by specific muscle weakness patterns.

*Kirlian photography*—a special photographic technique that shows up the energy field around the body, typically the hands.

*Laying-on-the-hands*— among the most direct approaches to healing. A "body therapy" for removing energy blockages, balancing, and improving one's healing journey through life.

*Lucid dreaming*—a type of dream state that is very clear and easily understood.

*Macrobiotics*—this Eastern philosophy is perhaps best known in the West through its dietary principles. The macrobiotic diet offers a way to achieve a fuller sense of balance both within ourselves and with the world around us by synchronizing our eating habits with the cycles of nature.

*Mandala*—Sanskrit word literally meaning "circle" or "center." A mandala consists of a series of concentric forms, suggestive of a passage between different dimensions. Through the mandala, man and woman may be projected into the universe and the universe into man and woman.

*Massage* —the application of dynamic pressure to the surface of the skin to stimulate physical reactions to correct disorders, to prevent sickness, and to promote good health.

*Meditation*—a state of focused attention through which one emerges into an ever-increasing clear awareness of reality. The deep relaxation of meditation heals the body, quiets the mind, and stimulates creativity and efficiency, thereby providing a sense of inner balance and peace.

*Metaphysics*—the systematic investigation of the nature of first principles and problems of ultimate reality.

*Metaphysical*—based on speculative or abstract reasoning.

*Miracle*—an event that appears unexplainable by the laws of nature and so is held to be supernatural or an act of God.

*Movement therapy*—a form of dance therapy.

*Natural (food)*—food that has not been refined or dramatically changed by industrial methods. It is often "organic," which means that the food has been grown without the use of any imbalanced fertilizers or harmful sprays.

*Network*—a link that binds us together, making it possible for us to share work, aspirations, and ideals. Networking is a process of making connections with other people.

*Neurological programming*—a comprehensive approach to developing more effective communication skills. Students learn how the understanding of language and behavior affects how we present ourselves and interact with others.

*New Age*—a term that has become widely used recently to describe some of the changes that are taking place in our world, and in our consciousnesses. With the year 2000, we will be entering another age, leaving the Piscean and entering the Aquarian.

*New Age music*—a synthesis of many different forms of music, resulting in a peaceful, somewhat "otherworldly" sound sometimes described as "spacey music."

*Nondenominational*—not pertaining to any particular group, organization, or religious tendency but rather encompassing them all.

*Past life therapy*—utilizes past life experiences and images to explore unconscious and conscious parts of ourselves in a manner similar to analyzing our dreams.

*Physical*—of or pertaining to the expression of the body.

*Podiatry*—the study and treatment of foot ailments.

*Polarity therapy*—a comprehensive and practical system of health developed by Randolph Stone. Polarity therapy coordinates diet, exercise, and techniques of body manipulation to increase and balance the flow of vital energy for the physical, emotional, and mental well-being of the individual.

*Psychic (development/readings/counseling)*—pertaining to the human mind or psyche; pertaining to the extraordinary, especially extrasensory and nonphysical, mental processes such as extrasensory perception and mental telepathy.

*Psychological*—of or involving the mind and the emotions.

*Purification*—to make or become clean or pure.

*Rebirthing*—a process that uses a simple, precisely defined circular breathing technique to enable the individual to achieve a finer awareness of mind, body, and emotions; to bring oneself fully into the present moment.

*Reflexology*—the theory of correspondence of reflex areas in the feet and hands to all areas of the body. Techniques of gentle stimulation of these reflexes directly act on particular organs and body parts to restore relaxation and balance.

*Regression therapy*—healing through being taken back to previous states, ages and/or conditions, the principle being to work through any traumatic and/or unresolved past experiences.

*Reiki*—meaning "universal life-force energy," a scientific method of activating and balancing the life-force energy present in all living things. Techniques applied to the entire body, channeling energy to organs and glands, and aligning the chakras (energy centers).

*Relaxation*—to become less formal or tense; to relieve from strain.

*Right/left brain integration*—the integration or balancing of the right, or "feminine," side of the brain with the left, or "masculine," side of the brain.

*Rolfing*—a complete Rolfing treatment consists of a series of ten sessions that progress from superficial to deeper layers of tissue and from localized areas of constriction to an overall reorganization of larger body segments.

*Sacred (sites)*—dedicated to or set apart for worship; worthy of reverence or respect; spiritual. Sacred sites are those places all over the world which are felt to be places of concentrated power and influence.

*Sauna*—a heat and bath treatment in which one is subjected to intense heat produced either by running water over heated rocks or by gently pouring water over heated rocks. Originated in Finland.

*Self-healing*—the art of healing oneself.

*Self-realization*—the quest for complete comprehension and understanding of who and what we are and why we are here.

*Shaman (shamanic)*—a Native American healer, wise person, or medicine person.

*Shiatsu*—using varying degrees of pressure to balance the life energy that flows through specific pathways in the body.

*Somatic*—of or pertaining to the body, especially as distinguished from a bodily part, the mind, or the environment.

*Sound vibration*—sound is the cause, not the effect, of vibration. Each one of us has our own vibrational pattern. When one centers and strengthens this pattern, one can draw strength and sustenance from the life system of which we are all a part. In the metaphysical sense, sound is the first principle, that which creates and destroys matter.

*Spa*— a mineral spring or a resort area with such a spring.

*Spiritual*—of or pertaining to the expression of the spirit.

*Stretching*—extending the body by a series of different bodily positions, with the aim of relieving stress and tension that can build up in the body.

*Stress*—physical, mental, emotional and/or spiritual fatigue and exhaustion.

*Sweat lodge*—ancient Native American ceremony involving the use of intense heat similar to that of a sauna and other methods to provoke visions and insights.

*Swedish massage*—consists of systematically applied scientific manipulations that gradually soothe the nervous and muscular systems and enhance general circulation.


*T'ai Chi*—a Chinese Taoist martial art form of "meditation in movement" which combines mental concentration, coordinated breathing, and a series of slow, graceful body movements.

*Tarot*—uses cards forming a series of transformative images whose origins are rooted in Western mystic tradition. Through these images, one may draw forth information from the unconscious, illuminating and clarifying the profound meaning of the moment in question.

*Therapeutic touch*—a form of laying on of the hands which creates a balance by transmitting energy and releasing energy blockages. It is a method of drawing and channeling the healing forces within and around us.

*Therapy*—the treatment of ill-health or dis-ability.

*Trager body work*—as developed by Milton Trager, this innovative approach to body work and movement education creates new possibilities in our ways of moving, thinking, and feeling.

*Transformation*—to change markedly.


*UFO*—unidentified flying object. Monitoring and recording of such objects is largely controlled by the military, and speculation has been growing about how much or how little the public is being told of their existence.


*Vegan*—a person who does not eat any animal products. The diet excludes all dairy, eggs, and honey.

*Vegetarian*—a person who does not eat any "meat," that is, any animal product that results from the killing of that animal.

*Vision quest*—a type of "rite of passage," based largely on Native American tradition, although similar rites of passage are practiced by many old native cultures. Most vision quests call for a period of time alone with nature.

*Western medicine*—for many years, based on an allopathic system culturally seen as a science of structural manipulation of a patient intended to "fight," conquer, and destroy disease. Hippocrates, who was born on the island of Cos in 460 B.C., is considered to be the father of Western medicine.

*Whole*—containing all component parts; complete.

*Wholistic*—See Holistic.

*Yoga*—the word "yoga" denotes a concept of discipline leading to union. The body and the mind form a continuum of consciousness and life that, when achieving a state of focus and clarity, may unite with Universal Spirit.

*Yurt*—circular canvas lodging, a sort of large ethnic tent.

Special thanks to Ken Pollinger at the New Age Center, for definitions of some of the terms. Thanks also to *The New Holistic Health Handbook, Wholistic Dimensions in Healing, Networking, the First Report and Directory,* and *Webster's Contemporary American Dictionary* for assistance with other definitions.

# About the Authors

Martine Rudee and Jonathan Blease formed *New Light Productions* in 1988 to produce a series of books on healing. They have been working together for the last three years and have been married since March 1987.

Martine is from the San Franscisco Bay area and Jonathan is from London, England. They have both studied and practiced many different forms of healing including yoga, nutrition, dance, medical herbalism, massage, music, astrology and tarot. Jonathan is also an agricultural graduate and Martine works with children. They are now living in Europe and compiling their next book, *Healing Centers and Retreats in Western Europe—A Traveler's Guide,* and working on another project in central and southern Africa.

# Traveler's Guide to Healing Centers and Retreats in North America Questionnaire

Name of Center/Retreat:

Address (include both mailing and street addresses if you wish both to be listed):

Telephone:

Person to Contact (and position/title):

Hours:

Founder/Date Founded:

Owner (if different from above):

Purpose of Center/Retreat:

Facilities:

Services Offered:

Visions and Goals:

Materials Available:

Other information you would like listed:

Consent: I hereby release the rights of all information contained in this questionnaire and any other materials (including photographs) submitted to New Light Productions and/or John Muir Publications for use in the updated edition of the *Traveler's Guide to Healing Centers and Retreats in North America.*

Signature:

Name (please print):

Title/Position:

Date:

# OTHER BOOKS FROM JOHN MUIR PUBLICATIONS

**22 Days Series: Travel Itinerary Planners**
These pocket-size guides are a refreshing departure from ordinary guidebooks. Each author has in-depth knowledge of the region covered and offers 22 carefully tested daily itineraries. Included are not only "must see" attractions but also little-known villages and hidden "jewels" as well as valuable general information. 128 to 144 pp., $7.95 each
**22 Days in Alaska** by Pamela Lanier (28-68-0)
**22 Days in the American Southwest** by Richard Harris (28-88-5)
**22 Days in Asia** by Roger Rapoport and Burl Willes (65-17-3)
**22 Days in Australia** by John Gottberg (65-03-3)
**22 Days in California** by Roger Rapoport (28-93-1)
**22 Days in China** by Gaylon Duke and Zenia Victor (28-72-9)
**22 Days in Europe** by Rick Steves (65-05-X)
**22 Days in France** by Rick Steves (65-07-6)
**22 Days in Germany, Austria & Switzerland** by Rick Steves (65-02-5)
**22 Days in Great Britain** by Rick Steves (28-67-2)
**22 Days in Hawaii** by Arnold Schuchter (28-92-3)
**22 Days in India** by Anurag Mathur (28-87-7)
**22 Days in Japan** by David Old (28-73-7)
**22 Days in Mexico** by Steve Rogers and Tina Rosa (65-04-1)
**22 Days in New England** by Anne E. Wright (28-96-6)
**22 Days in New Zealand** by Arnold Schuchter (28-86-9)
**22 Days in Norway, Denmark & Sweden** by Rick Steves (28-83-4)
**22 Days in the Pacific Northwest** by Richard Harris (28-97-4)
**22 Days in Spain & Portugal** by Rick Steves (65-06-8)
**22 Days in the West Indies** by Cyndy and Sam Morreale (28-74-5)

**"Kidding Around" Travel Guides for Children**
Written for kids eight years of age and older. Generously illustrated in two colors with imaginative characters and images. Each guide is an adventure to read and a treasure to keep.
**Kidding Around San Francisco,** Rosemary Zibart (65-23-8) 64 pp., $9.95
**Kidding Around Washington, D.C.,** Anne Pedersen (65-25-4) 64 pp., $9.95
**Kidding Around London,** Sarah Lovett (65-24-6) 64 pp., $9.95

**All-Suite Hotel Guide: The Definitive Directory,** Pamela Lanier
Pamela Lanier, author of The Complete Guide to Bed & Breakfasts, Inns & Guesthouses, now provides the discerning traveler with a listing of over 600 all-suite hotels. (65-08-4) 285 pp., $13.95

**Asia Through the Back Door,** Rick Steves and John Gottberg
Provides information and advice you won't find elsewhere—including how to overcome culture shock, bargain in marketplaces, observe Buddhist temple etiquette, and even how to eat noodles with chopsticks! (28-58-3) 336 pp., $11.95

**Buddhist America: Centers, Practices, Retreats,** Don Morreale
The only comprehensive directory of Buddhist centers, this guide includes first-person narratives of individuals' retreat experiences. (28-94-X) 312 pp., $12.95

**Bus Touring: Charter Vacations, U.S.A.,** Stuart Warren with Douglas Bloch
For many people, bus touring is the ideal, relaxed, and comfortable way to see America. Covers every aspect of bus touring to help passengers get the most pleasure for their money. (28-95-8) 200 pp., $9.95

**Catholic America: Self-Renewal Centers and Retreats,** Patricia Christian-Meyers
Complete directory of over 500 self-renewal centers and retreats in the United States and Canada. (65-20-3) 325 pp., $13.95

**Complete Guide to Bed & Breakfasts, Inns & Guesthouses in the United States and Canada,** 1989-90 Edition, Pamela Lanier
Newly revised and the most complete directory available, with over 5,000 listings in all 50 states, 10 Canadian provinces, Puerto Rico, and the U.S. Virgin Islands. (65-09-2) 520 pp., $14.95

**Elegant Small Hotels: A Connoisseur's Guide,** Pamela Lanier
This lodging guide for discriminating travelers describes hotels characterized by exquisite rooms and suites and personal service par excellence. (65-10-6) 230 pp., $14.95

**Europe 101: History & Art for the Traveler,** Rick Steves and Gene Openshaw
The first and only jaunty history and art book for travelers makes castles, palaces, and museums come alive. (28-78-8) 372 pp., $12.95

**Europe Through the Back Door,** Rick Steves
For people who want to enjoy Europe more and spend less money doing it. In this revised edition, Steves shares more of his well-respected insights. (28-84-2) 404 pp., $12.95
**Doubleday and Literary Guild Book Club Selection.**

**Gypsying After 40: A Guide to Adventure and Self-Discovery,** Bob Harris
Retirees Bob and Megan Harris offer a witty and informative guide to the "gypsying" life-style that has enriched their lives and can enrich yours. Their message is: "Anyone can do it!" (28-71-0) 312 pp., $12.95

**The Heart of Jerusalem,** Arlynn Nellhaus
Arlynn Nellhaus draws on her vast experience in and knowledge of Jerusalem to give travelers a rare inside view and practical guide to the Golden City. (28-79-6) 312 pp., $12.95

**Mona Winks: Self-Guided Tours of Europe's Top Museums,** Rick Steves and Gene Openshaw
Here's a guide that will save you time, shoe leather, and tired muscles. It is designed for people who want to get the most out of visiting the great museums of Europe. (28-85-0) 450 pp., $14.95

**The On and Off the Road Cookbook,** Carl Franz and Lorena Havens
A multitude of delicious alternatives to the usual campsite meals. (28-27-3) 272 pp., $8.50

**The People's Guide to Mexico,** Carl Franz
This classic guide shows the traveler how to handle just about any situation that might arise while in Mexico.
"The best 360-degree coverage of traveling and short-term living in Mexico that's going." — *Whole Earth Epilog* (28-99-0) 587 pp., $14.95

**The People's Guide to RV Camping in Mexico,** Carl Franz and Lorena Havens
This revised guide focuses on the special pleasures and challenges of RV travel in Mexico. Includes a complete campground directory. (28-91-5) 304 pp., $13.95

**The Shopper's Guide to Mexico,** Steve Rogers and Tina Rosa
The only comprehensive handbook for shopping in Mexico, this guide ferrets out little-known towns where the finest handicrafts are made and offers tips on shopping techniques. (28-90-7) 200 pp., $9.95

**Traveler's Guide to Asian Culture,** Kevin Chambers
An accurate and enjoyable guide to the history and culture of this diverse continent. (65-14-9) 356 pp., $13.95

**Traveler's Guide to Healing Centers and Retreats in North America,** Martine Rudee and Jonathan Blease
Over 300 listings offer a wide range of healing centers—from traditional to new age. (65-15-7) 224 pp., $11.95

**Undiscovered Islands of the Caribbean,** Burl Willes
For the past decade, Burl Willes has been tracking down remote Caribbean getaways. Here he offers complete information on 32 islands. (28-80-X) 220 pp., $12.95

**Automotive Repair Manuals**
Each JMP automotive manual gives clear step-by-step instructions together with illustrations that show exactly how each system in the vehicle comes apart and goes back together. They tell everything a novice or experienced mechanic needs to know to perform periodic maintenance, tune-ups, troubleshooting, and repair of the brake, fuel and emission control, electrical, cooling, clutch, transmission, driveline, steering and suspension systems and even rebuild the engine.
**How to Keep Your VW Alive** (65-12-2) 410 pp., $17.95
**How to Keep Your Golf/Jetta/Rabbit Alive** (65-21-1) 420 pp., $17.95
**How to Keep Your Honda Car Alive** (28-55-9) 272 pp., $17.95
**How to Keep Your Subaru Alive** (65-11-4) 420 pp., $17.95
**How to Keep Your Toyota Pick-Up Alive** (28-89-3) 400 pp., $17.95
**How to Keep Your Datsun/Nissan Alive** (28-65-6) 544 pp., $17.95
**How to Keep Your Honda ATC Alive** (28-45-1) 236 pp., $14.95

**Other Automotive Books**

**The Greaseless Guide to Car Care Confidence: Take the Terror out of Talking to Your Mechanic,** Mary Jackson
Teaches the reader about all of the basic systems of an automobile. (65-19-X) 200 pp., $14.95

**Off-Road Emergency Repair & Survival,** James Ristow
Glove compartment guide to troubleshooting, temporary repair, and survival. (65-26-2) 150 pp., $9.95

**Road & Track's Used Car Classics,** edited by Peter Bohr
Features over 70 makes and models of enthusiast cars built between 1953 and 1979. (28-69-9) 272 pp., $12.95

## Ordering Information

Fill in the order blank. Be sure to add up all of the subtotals at the bottom of the order form and give us the address whither your order is to be whisked.

## Postage & Handling

Your books will be sent to you via UPS (for U.S. destinations), and you will receive them in approximately 10 days from the time that we receive your order. Include $2.75 for the first item ordered and $.50 for each additional item to cover shipping and handling costs. UPS shipments to post office boxes take longer to arrive; if possible, please give us a street address.

For airmail within the U.S., enclose $4.00 per book for shipping and handling.

All foreign orders will be shipped surface rate. Please enclose $3.00 for the first item and $1.00 for each additional item. Please inquire for airmail rates.

## Method of Payment

Your order may be paid by check, money order, or credit card. We cannot be responsible for cash sent through the mail.

All payments must be made in U.S. dollars drawn on a U.S. bank. Canadian postal money orders in U.S. dollars are also acceptable.

For VISA, MasterCard, or American Express orders, use the order form or call (505)982-4078. Books ordered on American Express cards can be shipped only to the billing address of the cardholder. Sorry, no C.O.D.'s. Residents of sunny New Mexico, add 5.625% tax to the total.

## Back Orders

We will back order all forthcoming and out-of-stock titles unless otherwise requested.

All prices subject to change without notice.

**Address all orders and inquiries to:  John Muir Publications**
**P.O. Box 613**
**Santa Fe, NM 87504        (505)982-4078**

| ITEM NO. | | | TITLE | EACH | QUAN. | TOTAL |
|---|---|---|---|---|---|---|
| | | . | | | | |
| | | . | | | | |
| | | . | | | | |
| | | . | | | | |
| | | . | | | | |

Postage & handling (see ordering information)* _____

New Mexicans please add 5.625% tax _____

Total Amount Due _____

Credit Card Number: _____

Expiration Date: _____ Daytime telephone _____

Name _____

Address _____

City _____ State _____ Zip _____

Signature X _____

Required for Credit Card Purchases